Integrative Crisis Intervention
and
Disaster Mental Health

George S. Everly, Jr., PhD, ABPP
Center for Public Health Preparedness
The Johns Hopkins Bloomberg School of Public Health;
The Johns Hopkins School of Medicine; and
Loyola College in Maryland

And

Jeffrey T. Mitchell, PhD
Emergency Health Services
University of Maryland, Baltimore County

GW00676341

Integrative Crisis Intervention
and
Disaster Mental Health

© 2008 George Everly, Ph.D and Jeffrey T. Mitchell, Ph.D.
Published by Chevron Publishing Corporation
5018 Dorsey Hall Drive, Suite 104
Ellicott City, MD 21042

Printed in the United States of America
This book is printed on acid-free paper.

ISBN: 978-1-883581-12-1

CHEVRON
PUBLISHING CORPORATION

5018 Dorsey Hall Drive, Suite 104
Ellicott City, MD 21042 USA
Telephone: (410) 740-0065
Fax: (410) 740-9213

office@chevronpublishing.com

Integrative Crisis Intervention
and
Disaster Mental Health

About the Authors

George S. Everly, Jr., Ph.D., ABPP currently serves on the faculties of The Johns Hopkins University School of Medicine, The Johns Hopkins Center for Public Health Preparedness, The Johns Hopkins University Bloomberg School of Public Health, and Loyola College in Maryland. In addition he serves on the adjunct faculties of the Federal Emergency Management Agency, the FBI National Academy, and the U.S. Centers for Disease Control Mental Health Collaborative Committee. He is an advisor to the Hospital Authority of Hong Kong. He was formerly Senior Research Advisor, Social Development Office, Office of His Highness, the Amir of Kuwait, State of Kuwait. Prior to these appointments, Dr. Everly was a Harvard Visiting Scholar; a Visiting Lecturer in Medicine, Harvard Medical School; and Chief Psychologist and Director of Behavioral Medicine for the Johns Hopkins' Homewood Hospital Center.

Dr. Everly is a Fellow of the American Institute of Stress and has been awarded the Fellow's Medal of the Academy of Psychosomatic Medicine and the Professor's Medal of the Universidad de Weiner (Peru). He is the author, co-author, or editor of 14 textbooks and more than 100 professional papers. Among his texts are *Mental Health Aspects of Disasters: Public Health Preparedness and Response* (Johns Hopkins, 2005), *Pastoral Crisis Intervention* (Chevron, 2007), *Personality Guided Therapy of Posttraumatic Stress Disorder* (APA, 2004), *Critical Incident Stress Management, 2nd Edition*, with Jeffrey T. Mitchell (Chevron, 1999), *Psychotraumatology* (Plenum, 1995), *Critical Incident Stress Debriefing, 3rd Edition* with Jeffrey T. Mitchell (Chevron, 2001), *A Clinical Guide to the Treatment of the Human Stress Response, 2nd Edition* (Plenum, 2002), *Controlling Stress and Tension, 7th Edition* (Allyn Bacon, 2005), and *Personality and Its Disorders*, with Theodore Millon (Wiley, 1985).

Dr. Everly has won numerous awards receiving the Certificate of Honor from the Baltimore Police Department, the Honor Award from the American Red Cross, and the Maryland Psychological Association's Award for Scientific Contributions to Psychology. Dr. Everly was the recipient of the University of Maryland's College of

Health and Human Performance's 50th Anniversary Outstanding Alumni Award and was recognized as a "Pioneer in Clinical Traumatology" by the Traumatology Institute of the Florida State University. He served as the Mental Health Chairperson for the Central Maryland Chapter of the American Red Cross, where he was co-founder of the disaster mental health network. In addition, he assisted in the development of the State of Maryland Disaster Mental Health Corps and Maryland's Disaster Spiritual Care Corps. Dr. Everly was the 39th president of the Maryland Psychological Association. He has given invited lectures in 22 countries on 6 continents. His works have been translated into Russian, Arabic, Swedish, Polish, Portuguese, Japanese, Chinese, German, Korean, and Spanish. His biography appears in *Who's Who in America* and *Who's Who in the World.*

Jeffrey T. Mitchell, Ph.D., is a Clinical Professor of Emergency Health Services, University of Maryland and President Emeritus, International Critical Incident Stress Foundation. He is an adjunct faculty member in the Emergency Management Institute of the Federal Emergency Management Agency. He developed a comprehensive, integrated, systematic and multi-component crisis intervention program called "Critical Incident Stress management." He is a reviewer for the *Journal of the American Medical Association* (JAMA) and the *International Journal of Emergency Mental Health.* Since 1980, Dr. Mitchell has authored 14 books and more than 260 articles on traumatic stress, Critical Incident Stress Management, and crisis intervention. Dr. Mitchell, a recipient of the Austrian Red Cross Bronze Medal for his crisis intervention work, is a Fellow with the American Academy of Experts in Traumatic Stress and serves on AAETS's Board of Scientific and Professional Advisors. He is an Expert Consultant to the United Nations Department of Safety and Security Working Group on Stress.

The contents of this book are intended as a set of
guidelines. The book is not a substitute for formal
training, supervision, or field experience.

Table of Contents

Part One
Foundations

Part Two
Integrative Intervention

Part Three
Applications

PART ONE

Foundations

CHAPTER ONE

Foundations of Crisis Intervention and Disaster Mental Health

The words we choose to express a thought or capture a concept not only represent a medium of communication, but they affect the opinions we hold, the rhetoric we proffer, even the "science" we teach. Psycholinguistic scholar Benjamin Lee Whorf postulated, in the formulation of what was to be known as the Whorfian Hypothesis of Linguistic Relativity, that words have the power of shaping cognitive processes. In effect, words can shape how we think and the beliefs we hold. The poet T.S. Eliot once wrote that words decay with imprecision. It was George Engel, one of the pioneers in the field of psychosomatic medicine, who once said that a substantive issue in rational discourse is the need to use terms consistently. Surely no discussion of, no debate about theory or research, nor any conduct associated with inquiry regarding effective practice can be meaningful, nor anything but pseudo-science, without a definition of and agreement upon fundamental terms and concepts. Indeed, the foundation of all scientific inquiry is reliability. Unfortunately, the field of crisis intervention and disaster mental health has been made unnecessarily complicated because of an imprecise and unreliable utilization of even the most fundamental of terms. Therefore, as we begin this volume, we begin with an introduction to the terms we shall use throughout. The purpose of this book is to introduce the reader to recent conceptualizations and formulations regarding the psychosocial response to critical incidents, including large-scale and mass casualty disasters. Such formalized response has historically been referred to as the practice of crisis intervention and, when specifically applied to large-scale and mass casualty disasters, as disaster mental health. Let us take a closer look at these and other key formulations.

CRITICAL INCIDENTS

We begin with the term **critical incident**.

Critical incidents are stressful *events* which have the potential to overwhelm one's usual coping mechanisms resulting in psychological distress and an impairment of normal individual, as well as collective, adaptive functioning. Critical incidents may include individual or mass violence, medical emergencies, challenges to law and order, large-scale disasters that are natural- or human-induced, terrorism, and even warfare. But before exploring the response to critical incidents, let us review the nature of the challenge they represent. At the risk of oversimplification, we can say that there are three basic types of critical incidents:

- emergencies,
- disasters, and
- catastrophes (sometimes referred to as cataclysms).

All three are defined within the context of the demand they place upon the response systems they serve to challenge. Emergencies are events that result in either 1) physical destruction, or 2) injury to and/ or loss of human life. Of course, emergencies may involve both defining characteristics. They may serve to challenge but not exceed local emergency response capabilities (e.g., fire, emergency medical services, or n). Disasters are differentiated from emergencies largely by the magnitude of their impact; and typically, they may be thought of as events that result in a high magnitude of either physical destruction, injury to and/or loss of human life. Disasters cause disruption to social cohesion or community function and, by definition, exceed local emergency response capabilities. As a result, effective disaster response requires the recruitment of additional response capabilities and the added challenge associated with the leadership and the coordination of such resources. Finally, the catastrophe (cataclysm) is differentiated by its sheer magnitude of impact and may be thought of as an event that results in an overwhelming magnitude of physical destruction, injury to and/or loss of human life. The catastrophe will cause disruption to, if not elimination of, social cohesion and community function. The catastrophe will exceed all response capabilities. There are no direct mental health services provided in the acute phase of a catastrophe as survival becomes the highest priority.

PSYCHOLOGICAL CRISIS

The next key term to be discussed is **psychological crisis**.

Critical incidents may result in heroic actions and positive personal as well as communal/societal growth. However, the focus of this text will be upon the untoward reactions that arise from critical incidents and how to intervene prior to, during, and immediately following such incidents.

Let us now offer a working definition of a psychological crisis. As the body struggles to maintain a physical homeostasis (Cannon, 1932), or "steady state," so the mind struggles to maintain a similar balance. As a medical crisis is a state wherein physiological homeostasis has been disrupted with resultant physical distress and dysfunction, we then see the possibility of a psychological analogue. A **psychological crisis** is a *response* to a critical incident wherein the individual's psychological balance has been disrupted. There is, in effect, a psychological disequilibrium. This disequilibrium results because the individual's usual coping mechanisms have failed. The predictable result is the emergence of evidence of acute psychological or behavioral distress coupled with some degree of functional impairment.

More practically speaking, a crisis may be defined as a state of acute distress wherein one's usual coping mechanisms have failed in the face of a perceived challenge or threat and there results some degree of functional impairment (see Caplan, 1961, 1964). Caplan (1969) denoted two types of crises: 1) developmental, and 2) situational. Symptoms of a crisis condition may include:

- a range of affective presentations from panic to depression,
- cognitive dysfunctions,
- the presentation of a wide variety of physical complaints, and/or
- erratic or maladaptive behavior.

As we discuss definitions, it should be noted that the term **crisis** has been used to refer to both the *event* and the *response*, or reaction, to the event. Some authors even differentiate the term "psychological emergency" from "psychological crisis." According to Callahan (1998), the term psychological emergency is reserved for abrupt, specific situations where there is an "imminent risk of harm" (p. 23). A psychological crisis, however, "is generally nonspecific, is longer lasting, and does not include the risk of danger" (Callahan, 1998, p. 23). We find this differentiation somewhat arbitrary and contrary to the common practice of crisis intervention as observed by the present authors.

In contradistinction, the current definition of crisis offered in this volume does not differentiate dangerous from non-dangerous situations. Further, the current definition emphasizes the notion that a psychological crisis is the *reaction* to the critical incident (event). The roots of the current definition can be found in the work of Caplan (1961, 1964), yet the current conceptualization emphasizes, as the defining aspect of a crisis, *functional impairment in reaction to the event*. The degree of functional impairment can be extremely mild, or it can be severe and quite disabling. We believe the emphasis upon impairment is an important addition because it allows the crisis interventionist to conceptualize the goals of the acute intervention, that is, the reduction of acute distress, the restoration of adaptive functioning, or facilitation of access to continued care when necessary. We believe that an emphasis upon the psychological crisis being a reaction to a critical incident is an important distinction that has clinical relevance. For example, if the crisis is the event, then it may be seen as the *necessary and sufficient condition* to warrant the launching of crisis intervention services to *all* those in anyway involved. We worry that such a perspective could lead to an unnecessary deployment and implementation of psychological support services (Bisson, Brayne, Ochberg, & Everly, 2007). Such a condition could even serve to interfere with the natural resiliency mechanisms that most individuals will employ. However, if the crisis is seen as the reaction to the critical incident wherein one's usual coping mechanisms have failed and there is evidence of the impairment of adaptive functioning, then crisis intervention becomes need-based rather than event-based (Bisson, Brayne, Ochberg, & Everly, 2007). The roles of surveillance and assessment become not only essential but also self-evident from such a perspective. Furthermore, it becomes far easier to understand the value, if not the necessity, of community crisis intervention services long after the critical incidents themselves have passed.

CRISIS INTERVENTION

Our third term is the natural corollary of the psychological crisis…**crisis intervention.**

From an historical perspective, the provision of acute emergency psychological care has most often been referred to as crisis intervention. Indeed, crisis intervention is sometimes thought of as "emotional first-aid" (Neil, Oney, DiFonso, Thacker, & Reichart, 1974).

As used in this text, the term **crisis intervention** may be thought of as urgent psychological/behavioral care designed to first stabilize and then reduce symptoms of distress/dysfunction so as to achieve a state of adaptive functioning, or to facilitate access to continued care when necessary.

Crisis intervention is sometimes confused with counseling and psychotherapy. The P-I-E principles, derived and currently adapted from military psychiatry (Salmon, 1919; Artiss, 1963), may assist in this differentiation. P-I-E represents the defining characteristics of crisis intervention:

> P - proximity (the provision of services wherever needed),
> I - immediacy (urgency; rapid intervention as close to the emergence of adverse reactions as possible),
> E - expectancy (the view that the current state of disequilibrium is a result of a current perturbation; therefore, the goal of intervention is to address that current reaction, not cure any pre-existing psychiatric syndrome, even if it is present).

> Perhaps a useful way of conceptualizing crisis intervention is in the context of medical therapeutics. "As physuical first aid is to surgery, crisis intervention is to psychotherapy."

Thus, we see that by defining the nature of the problem, the goals of crisis intervention become more apparent. Simply stated, the goals of crisis intervention should include: 1) stabilization and mitigation of the individual's symptoms of acute distress, 2) restoration of a more "steady state" of psychological functioning (i.e.., psychological homeostasis), and 3) reduction of the level of manifest functional impairment, that is, to assist the person in returning to an adaptive level of functioning (see Artiss, 1963; Neil, Oney, DiFonso, Thacker, & Reichart, 1974; Caplan, 1964; Everly & Lating, 2002). When the goal of restoration of adaptive independent functioning is not deemed to be obtainable, it becomes the responsibility of the crisis interventionist to move the individual in crisis to a more advanced level of psychological care. It should be remembered that the focus of the intervention is always the present crisis reaction.

DISASTER MENTAL HEALTH

Disaster mental health may be thought of as the specific principles and practices of psychological crisis intervention, as well as clinical and community mental health, applied to large-scale and mass casualty disasters. Disaster mental health may be seen as a functional subset of psychological crisis intervention and as a clinical subspecialty thereof.

CONTINUUM OF CARE

A **continuum of care** may be thought of as a stepped progression of healthcare provided in an increasingly intensified manner.

In physical medicine, we see a progression from physical first aid, to basic life support, to advanced life support, to the practice of medicine and surgery, to rehabilitation.

In psychosocial intervention, we see a progression from crisis intervention (including its most elemental intervention referred to as "psychological first aid"), to more advanced crisis intervention, to counseling, to psychotherapy, to psychotropic medical practice, and to psychosocial rehabilitation. Crisis intervention, especially psychological first aid, is the entry point to the post-event psychosocial continuum of care, and can be the springboard to more advanced services. Thus, once again, we see that as physical first aid is to surgery, so crisis intervention is to psychotherapy.

THE EMERGENCE OF CRISIS INTERVENTION

Having defined the nature of crisis and crisis intervention, let us now turn to a review of the historical milestones relevant to the study of crisis intervention. The major milestones are summarized in linear form in Table 1.1.

Table 1.1
Historical Milestones in Crisis Intervention
and Disaster Mental Health

- **World War I** - The first empirical evidence arises indicating that early intervention reduces chronic psychiatric morbidity.
- **World War II** - The processes of proximity, immediacy, and expectancy are identified as important "active ingredients" in effective emergency psychological care.
- **1944** - Lindemann's observations of grief reactions to the Coconut Grove fire begins the "modem era" of crisis intervention.
- **late 1950s** - Community a prevention programs proliferate.
- **1963/64** - Caplan's three tiers of preventive psychiatry are delineated and implemented within the newly created community mental health system (primary, secondary, tertiary prevention).
- **late 1960s/early 1970s** - Crisis intervention principles are applied to reduce the need for hospitalization of potentially "chronic" populations.
- **1966** - At the University of Texas, Charles Whitman shot and killed 16 people from a clock tower on campus. He was ultimately shot by the police.
- **1980** - Formal recognition of posttraumatic stress disorder (PTSD) in DSM-Ill "legitimizes" crisis and traumatic events as threats to long-term mental health.
- **1982** - Air Florida 90 air disaster in Washington DC prompts reexamination of psychological support for emergency response personnel; it was the first mass disaster use of the group crisis intervention Critical Incident Stress Debriefing (CISD) which as originally formulated in 1974 by Mitchell (1983).
- **1986** – The "violence in the workplace" era began with death of 13 postal workers on the job.
- **1989** – The International Critical Incident Stress Foundation (ICISF) formalizes an international network of more than 350 crisis response teams trained in a standardized and comprehensive crisis intervention model referred to as Critical Incident Stress Management (CISM);ICISF gains United Nations affiliation in 1997.
- **1980s** – The National Organization for Victims Assistance (NOVA) provides crisis intervention and psychosocial support for crime victims and extends services to disaster victims.
- **1992** – The American Red Cross initiates formal training for the establishment of a nationwide disaster mental health capability; Hurricane Andrew tests new mental health function.
- **1993** – The Social Development Office (Amiri Diwan), ICISF, Kuwait University, et al., implement a nation-wide crisis intervention system for post-war Kuwait.
- **1994** – The DSM-IV recognizes Acute Stress Disorder and emphasizes impairment criterion in PTSD.
- **1995** – The bombing of the Federal Building in Oklahoma City underscores the need for crisis services for rescue personnel, as well as civilians.

Table 1.1 (cont.)

- **1996** – The TWA 800 mass air disaster emphasizes the need for emergency mental health services for families of the victims of traumas and disasters.
- **1996** - OSHA 3148-1996 recommends comprehensive violence/ crisis intervention in social service and healthcare settings.
- **1997** – The Gore Commission recommends crisis services for airline industry.
- **1998** - OSHA 3153-1998 recommends crisis intervention programs for late-night retail stores.
- **late 1990s** – Salvation Army initiates emotional and spiritual care for disaster victims.
- **April, 1999** – 14 students, including two shooters, are killed at Columbine High School in Littleton, Colorado.
- **2001** – Terrorist attacks at the Pentagon and World Trade Center in NYC reveal unique challenges associated with mass disasters in dense urban settings as well as challenges associated disasters involving terrorism.
- **2002** – Two snipers terrorize the northern Virginia and Washington, DC areas; the use of electronic town meetings emerges as a risk communication crisis intervention.
- **2003-2007** – The wars in Afghanistan and Iraq challenge the military to develop new crisis interventions (combat stress control).
- **August 2005** - Hurricane Katrina becomes one of the deadliest and the most costly natural disasters in American history; a putative failure in leadership leads to delayed and inadequate disaster response.
- **April 16, 2007** - The deadliest shooting in U.S. history occurred at Virginia Polytechnic Institute and State University. Thirty-three students and faculty members including the shooter were killed and at least 21 others were injured.
- **2007** – The United Nations adopts an integrated, multi-component critical incident stress management approach as the overarching intervention system for the psychosocial support of its own field personnel, thereby recognizing the importance of providing such support, as well as endorsing an integrated multi-component intervention systems' formulation.

The most significant of the early major milestones in the development of the field of crisis intervention can be found associated with warfare. T.W. Salmon (1919) made a significant contribution to the literature via his recollections and analyses of psychiatric emergencies during World War I. Salmon observed that the English and French medical corps had success in treating the various battlefield neuroses by moving their psychiatric facilities to more forward positions than were historically utilized and by employing stabilization and brief therapy procedures. He was finally able to argue that the American hospitals should do so as well. As a result of these changes, he observed a dramatic increase in the return-to-duty rates achieved by the end of the war.

From his work and that of Kardiner and Spiegel (1947), the three principles of crisis intervention - immediacy, proximity, and expectancy - were derived, articulated, and applied (Artiss, 1963; Solomon & Benbenishty, 1986; Solomon, Shklar, & Mikulincer, 2005).

Many modern writers point to Eric Lindemann's (1944) account of the November 28, 1943 Coconut Grove night club fire in Boston, wherein 492 people lost their lives, as the beginning of modern crisis intervention theory and practice. Lindemann's perspective on crisis intervention was the study and facilitation of the grief process subsequent to that catastrophic fire. Lindemann was later joined by Gerald Caplan in the creation of a community mental health program that emphasized community outreach and crisis intervention in the Boston metropolitan area.

Another important development in the early modem era of crisis intervention was the work of suicidologists Edwin Shneidman and Norman Farberow. In the mid 1950s, they created the prototype for suicide prevention centers in the United States in the form of the Los Angeles Suicide Prevention Center.

The field of crisis intervention received a major boost when, in 1963, President John Kennedy called for a "bold new approach" to the delivery of mental health services. The national Community Mental Health Centers Act was the result of that appeal. This congressional act established a network of community based mental health service centers wherein a major emphasis was placed upon crisis intervention services as a form of preventive outreach. Much of the conceptual foundation for this initiative was provided by the work of Caplan (1961, 1964), who delineated the three levels of preventive psychiatry. He defined preventive psychiatry as the body of knowledge designed to reduce "1) the incidence of mental disorders of all types in a community (primary prevention), 2) the duration of a significant number of those disorders which do occur (secondary prevention), and 3) the impairment which may result from those disorders (tertiary prevention)" (Caplan, 1964, p. 16-17). Crisis intervention, most typically, embodies Caplan's formulation of secondary prevention (Slaikeu, 1990).

As a result of the community mental health efforts, the 1960s and 1970s saw a proliferation of walk-in clinics and telephone hotlines. Clearly the heyday of fundamental crisis intervention services, this "first epoch" in community crisis intervention, saw the following advances:

- the provision of services within a prevention framework,
- deinstitutionalization of psychiatric services,
- aggressive community outreach,
- emphasis on brief intervention services as a viable mental health delivery paradigm, and
- the use of paraprofessional counselors.

The primary delivery systems during this "first epoch" in community crisis intervention were

- walk-in clinics and
- telephone hotlines.

The primary crisis intervention technologies employed during this "first epoch" in community crisis intervention were

- nondirective, client-centered counseling and
- basic problem solving and conflict resolution techniques.

As the 1970s ended and we entered the 1980s, enthusiasm in crisis intervention seemed to wane, even though considerable evidence had accumulated as to the efficacy of applied crisis theory and crisis intervention services (Decker & Stubblebine, 1972; Bordow & Porritt,

1979; Bunn & Clarke, 1979; Langsley, Machotka, & Flomenhaft, 1971; Parad & Parad, 1968). Thus, the first epoch in the history of crisis intervention drew to a close.

EMERGENCE OF DISASTER MENTAL HEALTH

As can be seen in Table 1.1, the field of psychological crisis intervention has existed since the early 1900s, yet the sub-specialty field of disaster mental health appears to have developed far more recently, since the early 1990s. The development of this field was due to a confluence of numerous factors, such as the recognition of the mental health consequences of mass disasters, an increase in global terrorism, the advent of the disaster mental health networks of the American Red Cross, the expanding presence of intervention teams from the National Organization for Victims' Assistance, the proliferation of Critical Incident Stress Management (CISM) teams affiliated with the International Critical Incident Stress Foundation, and the expansion of the Salvation Army's services to include disaster mental health and disaster spiritual health. These factors served to herald and similarly facilitate the growth and evolution of this new field. But it must be remembered that the initial development of any field is an imperfect process. As a result, it would be expected that both tactical and strategic modifications should naturally occur over time and when confronted by challenging field applications. Responding to the more recent mass disasters and the on-going conflicts in the Middle East, the field of disaster mental health has experienced changes in both tactical implementation and strategic planning. Tactically, many interventions have undergone reconsideration and operational alterations since their initial development. Similarly, they have become increasingly innovative in order to respond to the plethora of situational complexities often associated with mass disasters. Strategically, mass disasters and warfare, especially the war in Iraq, demand the most sophisticated levels of strategic planning for the disaster mental health response, this due to the confluence of multi-dimensional needs demanding an integrated, multi-faceted mental health response (Raphael, 1986, Everly & Mitchell, 1999; Ritchie, Friedman, Watson, Ursano, Wessely, & Flynn, 2004; US Dept of Heath & Human Services, 2004; Sheehan, Everly, & Langlieb, 2004; Ruzek, Young, Cordova, & Flynn, 2004).

CRITICAL INCIDENT STRESS MANAGEMENT (CISM)

It may be said that crisis intervention and disaster mental health represent a mental health specialization that continues, even today, to quantitatively expand and qualitatively evolve. For this evolutionary process to continue successfully, a second epoch of greater sophistication must be realized both tactically and strategically. Long gone are the days when crisis intervention consisted solely of telephone hotlines and walk-in crisis clinics. Long gone are the days when a small group discussion, referred to as Critical Incident Stress Debriefing (CISD), was the only viable disaster mental health intervention. The purpose of this volume is not only to review the evolving nature of crisis intervention and emergency/disaster mental health, but also to offer an integrative and comprehensive paradigm for the provision of crisis intervention and disaster mental health services. It is hoped that such a paradigm not only will serve to advance the field of crisis and disaster mental health, but also will serve as a viable standard of care in crisis intervention for the new millennium.

The British Psychological Society (1990) recommended that crisis intervention techniques be combined. We agree. Mitchell and Everly (1996) argued for an even more highly integrated combinatorial program to insure the potency of the intervention. Bordow and Porritt (1979) were presumably the first to actually demonstrate, in a well-controlled investigation, the dose-response potency of combined crisis intervention technologies (also see Solomon & Benbenishty, 1986;

Solomon, Shklar, & Mikulincer, 2005), such as we see in CISM. Thus, the natural corollary of the critical incident at the strategic level is Critical Incident Stress Management (CISM).

As defined by Mitchell and Everly (1996), Critical Incident Stress Management (CISM) represents an integrated and comprehensive multi-component approach to the provision of crisis intervention and disaster mental health services.

The CISM formulation is actually broader and more comprehensive in scope than the historical applications of crisis intervention and is more consistent with Caplan's comprehensive (1961, 1964) formulations of preventive psychiatry. Specifically, CISM embodies

- primary prevention (i.e., the identification and mitigation of pathogenic stressors),
- secondary prevention (i.e., the identification and mitigation of acute distress and dysfunctional symptom patterns), and
- tertiary prevention (i.e., follow-up mental health treatment and rehabilitation services).

Thus, the specific goals of the CISM program are

- to reduce
  the duration of,
  the severity of, or
  the impairment from traumatic stress arising from crisis situations, and
- to facilitate advanced follow-up mental health interventions when necessary.

In the final analysis, the ultimate goal of CISM is the mitigation of acute, disabling psychological discord and the rapid restoration of adaptive functioning in the wake of a critical (crisis) incident.

Thus CISM represents an amalgam of specific crisis- and disaster-related interventions. CISM is the embodiment of the psychological continuum of care. Its primary components will be discussed in detail in a later chapter, but will be simply listed here in preface within Table 1.2.

Table 1.2
Critical Incident Stress Management (CISM)

1. Pre-event Planning/ Preparation
2. Surveillance & Assessment
3. Strategic planning
4. Individual Crisis Intervention
5. Large Group Crisis Intervention (demobilizations, respite sectors, large group crisis management briefings)
6. Small Group Crisis Intervention [immediate small group support or defusings, Critcal Incident Stress Debriefings or Powerful Event Group Support, and small group crisis management briefings]
7. Family Crisis Intervention
8. Organizational / Community Intervention.
9. Pastoral Crisis Intervention
10. Follow – up, referral. Facilitation of access to continued care

CISM is the embodiment of Millon's formulation of integrative psychological services. According to Millon, Grossman, Meagher, Millon, and Everly (1999), "The palette of methods and techniques available to the [interventionist] must be commensurate with the idiographic heterogeneity of the [individuals] for whom the methods and techniques are intended" (1999, p. 145). Ultimately, such an approach to intervention formulation would lead the interventionist to choose the best therapeutic intervention, or set of therapeutic interventions, to meet the needs of the individual at that present point in time.

According to Watson and Shalev (2005), "Early intervention in mass traumatic events should be embedded within a multidisciplinary, multi-tiered disaster mental health system. Early interventions should be utilized in a culturally sensitive manner, related to the local formulation of problems and ways of coping, and applied flexibly, in ways that match needs and situational context and take into account the ongoing stressors, reactions, and resources" (p. 123).

EVOLVING GOALS

Setting appropriate goals for psychological crisis intervention and disaster mental health must be based upon a realistic formulation of what such interventions are and what they are not. Conceptually, as noted earlier, a parallel may be drawn between physical health and mental health such that "as physical first aid is to surgery, psychological crisis intervention is to psychotherapy."

As the goals of physical first aid are

- stabilization of physiological functioning,
- mitigation of physiological dysfunction/ distress,
- return of acute adaptive physiological functioning, and/or
- facilitation of access to the next level of car;

the goals of psychological crisis intervention and disaster mental health are

- stabilization of psychological functioning through meeting basic physical needs, then addressing the most basic of psychological needs,
- mitigation of psychological dysfunction/ distress,
- return of acute adaptive psychological functioning, and/or
- facilitation of access to the next level of care.

Early psychological intervention is not psychotherapy, nor is it a substitute for psychotherapy. Deahl (2000) has argued that early psychological intervention research is contaminated with the assumption that the outcome goals (and thereby the expectations) for early psychological intervention are commonly confused with the same outcome goals for "treatment." Thus, the prevention/eradication of PTSD or depression may be an unfair expectation; that expectation therefore seems inappropriate.

More specifically, as early psychological interventions such as disaster mental health initiatives were being originally formulated, lofty or overly simplistic expectations were sometimes implicitly or explicitly applied. Initially, some believed that early psychological disaster response might exert a preventive effect so as to block the development of posttraumatic stress disorder (PTSD) and other psychiatric reactions such as major depression (Mitichell & Everly, 1993; Everly, 1995).

Research has yet to convincingly demonstrate such a global preventive effect (Arendt & Elklit, 2001; Professional Practice Board Working Party, 2002). Arendt & Elklit (2001), in a review of more than two dozen controlled trials of early psychological intervention (generically referred to as "debriefing"), concluded that the prevention of PTSD seems an inappropriate expectation and such an expectation may be a potential disservice to the field of early psychological intervention, with the possible exception of instances in which such interventions are employed with emergency services personnel. Again, the eradication of PTSD would seem an inappropriate expectation. A more appropriate expected outcome might be screening for as well as possible *mitigation* of posttraumatic distress. Ursanoand colleagues (2003) note, "Multiple outcomes are of importance following disasters and terrorism and need to be examined for various types of interventions...Interventions that foster return of function, even though they may not directly prevent psychiatric illness, may be of importance" (p. 336). Deahl and his colleagues (Deahl, et al., 2001; Deahl, 2000) have similarly argued that expectations for early psychological intervention should not be focused solely upon PTSD. They noted that early psychological intervention may positively affect other aspects of posttraumatic illness (PTI) that typically go unmeasured. They cite, in support of such a conclusion, their own randomized controlled trial of early intervention (specifically Critical Incident Stress Debriefing, CISD) which found a reduction of posttraumatic alcohol use in soldiers returning from a peace-keeping mission in eastern Europe (Deahl, et al., 2000).

Interestingly, Flannery and his colleagues have developed an integrated Critical Incident Stress Management (CISM) intervention program, referred to as the Assaulted Staff Action Program (ASAP), which has consistently shown effectiveness in reducing patient assaults upon institutional hospital staff (Flannery, 2001; Flannery, Hanson, Penk, Flannery, & Gallagher, 1995; Flannery, Penk, & Corrigan, 1999). According to Caplan (1964), the seminal writer in the field of modern psychological crisis intervention, a reasonable expectation for "prevention" would include *mitigation of symptoms, the reduction of dysfunction, and even the fostering of healthy coping behaviors.*

SUMMARY

In this chapter, we have traced the historical roots of crisis intervention and disaster mental health. We have proposed that the history of this specialty within clinical mental health services is actually marked by two eras, or epochs.

Epoch One saw the advent of the notions of community outreach and preventive mental health services, as well as the use of paraprofessionals. Epoch Two saw the increasing sophistication with which the concepts of Epoch One were applied in the form of a multi-component, integrated system of service provision that comprehensively spans the entire crisis spectrum, from pre-crisis planning and on-scene support services through referral for advanced mental health assessment and treatment, if necessary.

CHAPTER TWO

Terrorism: A Unique Form of Critical Incident

George S. Everly, Jr. and Jeffrey M. Lating

At the end of the last century international terrorist groups declared war on the United States. Rather than pursue this war using conventional means, terrorist tactics have been employed. On the five year anniversary of the worst terrorist attack in the United States, President George W. Bush said the war against terrorism is "the calling of our generation." President Bush went on to say, "America did not ask for this war, and every American wishes it were over…The war is not over - and it will not be over until either we or the extremists emerge victorious." We contend that terrorism is primarily a psychological agent and as such is relevant to the study and formulation of crisis intervention and disaster mental health programs.

DEFINING TERRORISM

The way in which one defines a phenomenon serves to dictate how one understands and interacts with that phenomenon. Thus, how we define terrorism serves to set the stage for how we prepare for and respond to acts of terrorism. Terrorism may be understood from several perspectives:

- From a law enforcement perspective, terrorism may be thought of as the premeditated and unlawful use, or threatened use, of force or violence as a coercive or punitive agent.

- From a military perspective, terrorism represents war waged against civilians (Carr, 2002).
- From a psychological/behavioral perspective, terrorism represents psychological warfare with no apparent moral, ethical, or legal constraints. Terrorism can be used as a tool to break down the resistance and diminish the will of a population and/or its government (Everly & Castellano, 2005).

Thus, terrorism represents psychological warfare, not traditional military combat. Threats of assassination, bioterrorism, and even nuclear detonations have been used. Numerous attacks have subsequently been realized against both domestic and international targets. Winning the war against terrorism means acknowledging and responding to the psychological dynamics inherent in this form of warfare, as well as the military and law enforcement aspects of the war. Consistent with Caplan's notions of preventive psychiatry, the fight against terrorism must occur on three levels: 1) prevention of the terrorist attacks themselves, 2) mitigation of the adverse psychological impact of the persistent threats of terrorist acts, as well as the terrorist attacks when they do occur, and 3) psychological treatment of the lingering adverse effects of threatened or actualized terrorist attacks. The preplanned and/or coordinated psychological efforts to counteract terrorism and prevail in any given war against terrorism shall be discussed herein and subsequently referred to as "psychological counterterrorism."

PSYCHOLOGICAL TOXICITY

As noted above, the goal of terrorism is to demoralize and diminish resistance. Terrorism may consist of aversive actions or merely the threat of such actions. As the great military strategist Sun Tzu (Clavell, 1983) noted, "To fight and conquer in all your battles is not supreme excellence; supreme excellence consists in breaking the enemy's resistance without fighting" (p. 15). The direct physical target of the terrorist act is seldom the actual target by design; rather it is but the means to an end...the end state of breaking the enemy's will. In the case of terrorism, the "psychological casualties" will outnumber the "physical casualties;" this by design (IOM, 2003).

Terrorism targets:

Your sense of safety ("I'm affraid to do what I normally do.")
Your sense of justice and fair play ("That's not right, fair...")
Your sense of order or meaning ("It doesn't make sense...How could anyone do such a thing?")

The adverse impact of terrorism may, therefore, be estimated not just in terms of physical destruction, but also in terms of psychological "toxicity." Factors that may serve to increase psychological toxicity might include

- an unpredictable pattern of attacks;
- the ability to affect large numbers of victims;
- the intent to harm noncombatants, especially targeting women and children;
- the ease of weapon delivery;
- a delay and difficulty in assessing exposure, especially lethality;
- a long latency or incubation period, at least several days;
- a potential for contagion (physical or psychological), especially if it deters emergency response and/or treatment;
- a potential to scar and disable rather than kill;
- the ability to overwhelm public health and other resources, while altering the accepted and preferential way of life;
- a motivation which is immune to rational, measured deterrence;
- a willingness to use self-destruction as a weapon; and/or
- "all or nothing" strategic thinking.

TERRORISM AND TOTAL WAR

Total war is a concept first described by Carl von Clausewitz in a book entitled *Vom Kriege (On War)* published in 1832. Though not originally described as such, for some the concept has come to embody a deadly extreme…attack anything associated with the enemy…attack the sacred, attack the strategic sources of power, kill the innocent, do the unthinkable, demoralize until the enemy capitulates. The two points to remember here are 1) that terrorism may be fought as a form of total warfare, having no limitations, no boundaries; 2) total warfare may lead to an escalating spiral wherein "mutually assured destruction" is actually realized (especially in a war that is fought on religious grounds and martyrdom is a recognized virtue).

PSYCHOLOGICAL CONTAGION

Considering that a primary goal of terrorism is to create pervasive fear and uncertainty among its survivors, the theory of contagion and managing its effects warrants exploration. The term "contagion" has typically been associated with medical diseases, mostly infectious agents, and refers to transmission of disease by direct or indirect contact, or "something that serves as a medium to transmit disease" (Merriam-Webster's Collegiate Dictionary, Tenth Ed.). In the present context, psychological contagion refers to how the effects of terrorism are transmitted to those not directly affected by the initial event. In essence, it represents a surge of events, both behavioral and psychological, that threaten our safety and security (Everly & Castellano, 2005).

Pfefferbaum and Pfefferbaum (1998) have proposed how the concept of contagion may clarify some important aspects of PTSD. As noted, from an infectious disease model, a contagion is transmitted either directly or indirectly. Similarly, the DSM IV diagnostic criteria for PTSD provide for both direct exposure to the traumatic event (as a victim or a witness) and indirect modes of transmission. These latter transmissions may occur through emotional proximity (e.g., learning that a family member or close friend was involved in a traumatic incident), exposure to the symptoms of afflicted others (e.g., vicarious traumatization), the enduring impact of stress following a far-reaching community event (i.e., community contamination), and the media's overexposure of provocative material. Pfefferbaum and Pfefferbaum (1998) offered an infectious disease model to address primary (i.e., alter susceptibility of exposure), secondary (i.e., early detection and treatment), and tertiary (i.e., limiting disability and fostering rehabilitation) prevention, control, and treatment of PTSD.

Bioterrorism and Contagion Theory

Given terrorism's potential to create large-scale psychological morbidity, from a contagion perspective there are no more potentially devastating terrorist weapons than biological, chemical, or nuclear agents. The implementation of biological agents against a human population, referred to as bioterrorism, is associated with our most fundamental fears of disease and death. Bioterrorist events, due to their possible invisible nature, extreme lethality, long incubation time, and lack of defined perimeter, clearly expose our societal vulnerability.

The exposure to inhalation anthrax, experienced shortly after September 11, is just one of many potentially daunting biological agents. Related to anthrax, a portentous 1993 prediction from the Office of Technology Assessment of the U.S. Congress estimated that dispersal of 100 kilograms of anthrax spores from an airplane flying over Washington, DC on a calm night could kill more than one million people (U.S. Congress, 1993). Others agents include 1) botulism, a muscle-paralyzing bacterial disease that can be caused from eating contaminated food, 2) plague (caused by Yersinia pestis), a contagious form of bacterial pneumonia that could be spread from an aerosol release, 3) smallpox, which is an acute, virally contagious, and sometimes fatal disease (in approximately 30% of cases) that is marked by a progressive skin rash (spotted, raised bumps on the face and body) and fever, and is prevented by vaccination, 4) tularemia, a very infectious bacteria that could be spread from an aerosol release, and 5) sarin, an extremely toxic clear, colorless substance that disables the nervous system. Sarin was responsible for the death of 12 people and the injury, or suspected injury, of more than 5,500 (mostly with headache, coughing, nausea, cardiac symptoms, neuropathy) when it was released by members of the Aum Shinrikyo cult in a Tokyo subway during rush hour in March 1995. More specifically, cult members placed sealed plastic bags of diluted sarin onto the subway trains and then pierced the bags with sharpened umbrella tips before leaving the train (Bowler, Murai, & True, 2001).

Since society, including most relevantly the medical community, has had little formal experience in treating the illnesses caused by these agents (i.e., who will become ill and for how long), apprehension and fear related to their exposure is especially heightened (Ursano, Norwood, Fullerton, Holloway, & Hall, 2003). These agents are associated with pain, suffering, disfigurement, and death. Medical treatment may have limited effectiveness, particularly if the agent is unknown, as it was for three hours after the sarin gas attack in Japan, or if the substance has been modified.

Clearly an intentional bioterrorist attack using any one, or a combination of these agents and/or other agents, is likely to have profound medical effects. However, the psychological impact may be equally as daunting. Consider, for example, that in addition to the physical injuries reported from the sarin gas attacks, there were considerable symptoms of psychological distress among its victims. Within weeks of the attacks, 60% of surveyed victims had symptoms consistent with PTSD (nightmares, flashbacks, intrusion, and avoidance; Asukai, 1999), and fours years after the attacks, 57% of victims who responded to a survey continued to have symptoms of depression, flashbacks, nightmares, and panic when boarding trains (Watts, 1999). Also of note, Watts reported that lack of knowledge regarding the long-term effects of sarin gas added to the public's already heightened sense of distress. As noted by Birchard (1999), lack of conviction on the part of health officials to give blanket assurances that no harm will come from brief or non-symptom-resulting exposure to any chemical, radiological, or biological materials will likely result in mistrust in the reporting agencies. Furthermore, the likely dissemination of differing opinions by credible experts regarding possible health effects of exposure may create even more controversy and distrust.

Empirical Studies supporting Contagion and Terrorism

Although not designed specifically to address the potential effects of psychological contagion, studies conducted on samples of the population in the aftermath of September 11 exemplify the concept indirectly. For example, Galea and colleagues (2002), in a random telephone sample of 1008 adults between five and nine weeks after the attacks and living south of 110th Street in Manhattan (which is approximately eight miles north of the World Trade Center), found that 7.5% of the participants reported symptoms of PTSD, whereas 20.0% of the sample living south of Canal Street (near the World Trade Center) reported PTSD symptoms.

In another study, Schlenger and his colleagues (2002), in a web-based survey of 2273 adults, reported PTSD prevalence rates of 11.2% in New York City, 2.7% in Washington, DC, 3.6% in other major metropolitan areas, and 4.0% for the rest of the country. These data suggest that those living in New York City, and more specifically, those living closest to the World Trade Center, may be more at risk for developing PTSD symptoms in the wake of September 11 than those living farther away. There may be many reasons why geographic differences occurred in these representative samples of the general population, including the perception of more imminent threat due to physical proximity to the major bombing site. However, the comparatively low incidence of PTSD symptoms in Washington, DC seems inconsistent with this claim. A possible reason for the inconsistencies may be that physical proximity to the attacks may not be the most salient virulent factor in accounting for the PTSD symptoms. Instead, is it possible that the randomly sampled population in DC interpreted the attack on the Pentagon as aimed at a military target? If so, then the attacks may have been interpreted as less personally relevant than the civilian target of the World Trade Center, where a common response may be have been, "This could have been happened to me." In other words, is perceived personal threat the most salient virulent medium associated with the possible spread of psychological contagion?

Support for this contention can be found in a work published more than 60 years ago. Agnes McClure (1943) used a sample of 379 teachers, assessing their anonymous ratings of children from 69 London elementary schools located in areas that were badly bombed, slightly damaged, or unharmed in the aftermath of repeated air raids during World War II. It is worth noting that the areas labeled "unharmed," due to the lack of property damage or loss of life, were located only five to six miles from the raids, so the noise from the raids could be heard clearly. Moreover, in the days following the raids, rumors occurred regarding pending attacks on the unharmed areas. The teachers who participated in the study completed a 17-item questionnaire designed to assess behaviors and cognitive functions observable in their students. The items included assessed fidgetiness, quarrelsomeness, concentration, noisiness, and physical weariness. The overall results indicated that reactions were the same in the undamaged areas as in those areas badly bombed. Therefore, physical proximity to the event did not seem to be the primary predictor of adverse reactions; this led McClure (1943) to conclude that the symptoms seemed to be more related to concomitant factors, "including psychological contagion" (p .29), than to the raids themselves.

Another example of a possible psychological contagion effect occurred during the Iraqi scud missile attacks on Israel during the

Persian Gulf War. In preparation for possible attacks, gas masks and atropine, an antidote for exposure to biochemicals, were distributed to the entire population of Israel. Between January 16 and February 28, 1991, 39 missiles were launched, with six causing direct casualties. Other missiles either exploded in the air, fell in non-residential areas, or fell into the sea (Karsentry et al., 1991). Despite the attacks, relatively few people were injured. Out of the 1,059 war-related hospital admissions, only 22% were directly injured, with two deaths occurring due to falling building debris. From a psychological contagion perspective, however, there were 825 indirect casualties, which resulted in more deaths than the direct injuries did. Specifically, seven people died from suffocation due to faulty use of gas masks (leaving the filter closed), and four died of heart attacks. Furthermore, 230 patients needlessly injected themselves with the atropine, and 40 sustained injuries, ranging from superficial cuts to leg fractures, while rushing to get to the shelter after hearing the alert signal. Moreover, according to Shalev and Solomon (1996), "during this time, an astonishing 544 patients were admitted to hospital emergency wards throughout the country with symptoms of acute psychological distress" (p.150-151).

A survey of 108 Kuwaiti firefighters four and a half years after the Iraqi from Kuwait provides additional corroboration of the psychological contagion effect (Al-Naser & Everly, 1999). Of the 18.5% of the entire sample with symptoms consistent with PTSD, there was no difference in prevalence between those firefighters who were in Kuwait during the Iraqi invasion and those who were not.

Although not specifically designed to assess the theory of psychological contagion, some data from the sarin gas attack in Tokyo that was addressed previously also support the phenomenon. Ohbu and colleagues (1997), who studied 641 patients on the day of the disaster, reported that 531 patients (83%) were classified as "mild," meaning they were treated in the outpatient department and released after six hours of observation. According to Ursano, Norwood,

Fullertion, Holloway, and Hall, the preponderance of the 5,500 patients who sought medical care had no sign of exposure, and "many misattributed the signs and symptoms of anxiety and autonomic arousal to intoxication by sarin" (2003, p.142).

In the aftermath of the anthrax attacks soon after September 11, a wave of contagious anxiety led to mass psychogenic illness. In the weeks following the initial confirmed case that killed a Florida man, there were more than two thousand false anthrax reports (Roan, 2001). Additionally, in Ontario, Canada, in the week after the first reported case, there was an increase in written prescriptions for the antibiotic Cipro (used to treat anthrax exposure), despite restrictive policies that required physicians to justify its use (Austin, Mamdani, Jaakkimainen, & Hux, 2002). In response to this demand, which included the subsequent phenomenon of medication hoarding, Dr. Donald Shifrin stated that "fear is much more contagious than microbes" (abcNEWS.com, 2001, ¶ 2).

In a study designed specifically to examine the psychological contagion phenomenon, Lating, Sherman, Lowry, Everly, and Peragine (2004) assessed psychological reactions and functional coping responses of American Airlines (AA) East Coast and West Coast flight attendants after the attacks of September 11. AA flight attendants are a particular "at-risk" population in the war on terrorism. Flight 11 and Flight 77, the ones deliberately crashed into the World Trade Center's North Tower and the Pentagon, respectively, on September 11, Flight 587, which crashed shortly after takeoff from New York on November 12, 2001, and Flight 63, noted for the presence of the "shoe bomber," were all AA planes. In an effort to assess functioning of AA flight attendants, demographics and standardized questionnaires were received from 2,050 flight attendants from bases located throughout the country. The returned surveys were separated into East Coast (513 from Boston, New York, and Washington, DC) and West Coast (353 from Los Angeles and San Francisco) in order to assess similarities and differences in emotional reactions and functioning. Despite demographic differences between the flight crew members, most notably the fact that the East Coast flight crews knew more than twice the number of people who perished as a result of September 11 or the subsequent crash of Flight 587 than the West Coast flight crews (69% vs. 30%), there were no statistically significant differences between them in the amount of probable PTSD (19.1% and 18.3%, respectively) or life functioning. These data support the notion stated earlier, that personal relevance may be the mechanism of virulence in spreading a possible psychological contagion.

In a more recent study that sought to expand these findings, Lating, Sherman and Peragine (2006) created an additional comparison group consisting of current AA flight attendants not working on either the East Coast or the West Coast and who were also previously working for Trans World Airlines (TWA) prior to AA assuming operating authority in April 2001. Of the 73 participants who met these criteria, 26% knew someone who perished as a result of September 11 or Flight 587, which is statistically comparable to the West Coast flight crews from AA. Moreover, and additionally supportive of the contagion theory, 15.1% of the former TWA flight attendants had probable PTSD, which was not significantly different from the AA East Coast and West Coast flight attendants.

PSYCHOLOGICAL COUNTERTERRORISM AND EARLY PSYCHOLOGICAL INTERVENTION

Psychological counterterrorism may be thought of as the preplanned and/or coordinated psychological efforts to counteract terrorism and prevail in any given war against terrorism.

Consistent with the crisis intervention work of Caplan (1964), psychological counterterrorism may be manifest within the first two of three operational initiatives: 1) psychological efforts to prevent terrorist acts, 2) psychological efforts to mitigate the adverse impact of threatened or realized terrorist acts, and 3) psychological efforts to treat and rehabilitate those adversely effected by terrorism (Everly & Castellano, 2005).

Psychological Efforts to Prevent Terrorism

Psychological efforts to prevent terrorism fall into three domains:

- Efforts to remove terrorism as a tactical option by having the global society view it with such legal, moral, and political distain that it is simply not considered as a viable option for any organized society or social movement. This must be true for those who would consider using terrorism and for those who would support terrorism.
- Psychological "immunization" of any given target population.
- Establishment of a condition wherein "justice" is perceived to be available to all.

Psychological Efforts to Mitigate the Adverse Impact of Terrorism

Psychological efforts to mitigate the adverse effects of terrorism may include:

- Provision of pre-incident training and education.
- Provision of "acute psychological first aid"
- Provision of community "town meetings" (either in person or using electronic media) to provide relevant operational updates, health education, and stress management. Town meetings may also be used to control rumors, build/sustain community cohesion, and foster personal and community empowerment.
- Implementation of an integrated, multi-component system of crisis intervention and disaster mental health services, as available and as indicated.

Psychological Efforts to Treat and Rehabilitate Those Adversely Affected

Psychological efforts to treat and rehabilitate those most adversely affected by terrorism may include individual and group psychotherapy, psychopharmacologic interventions, and even acute custodial care.

SUMMARY

Terrorism represents a unique form of critical incident. As such, it may be the single most severe form of stressor to be challenged by any early psychological response system. Using the pioneering crisis intervention work of Caplan (1964) as a framework, early psychological intervention becomes a form of psychological counterterrorism that may be embodied within two of the three aforementioned operational initiatives: 1) psychological efforts to prevent terrorist acts, and 2) psychological efforts to mitigate the adverse impact of threatened or realized terrorist acts. Here the importance of integrative crisis and disaster mental health becomes apparent. In the final analysis, the war on terrorism will be won or lost in the minds of those who are the targets of the terrorism itself. Increasing psychological resistance and resiliency must be part of any national defense plan as well as any national public health initiative. Security is, after all, a state of mind.

CHAPTER THREE

Mental Health Aspects of Crisis and Disaster

In the previous chapters, we introduced the foundational terms and concepts necessary to the study of crisis intervention and disaster mental health. A key concept to be noted is that the focus of inquiry as well as intervention needs to be the response to critical incidents, not the critical incidents themselves. Rather, critical incidents are best understood by virtue of their toxic qualities and their effects, not their superficial nature. In this chapter, we shall examine the mental and behavioral consequences of critical incidents.

Everyone will experience disturbances in their daily routines, lifestyles, and/or careers. Whether these disturbances are experienced as personal crises, as we have earlier defined them, is but a matter of the degree, or intensity, of their felt impact.

The perspective taken by this volume denotes a crisis as a significant inability to cope with a developmental or situational challenge such that one may be left overwhelmed, confused, and feeling defenseless against the challenge. Perhaps most importantly, however, crisis creates a condition wherein the individual experiences some degree of psychological and/or behavioral impairment (dysfunction). As noted earlier, clinically speaking, the nature and severity of the impairment is the most salient feature of the overall crisis complex. The impairment of human functioning has serious implications not only for the individual but also for every context within which that individual functions.

Therefore, the impact of crisis can easily extend beyond the individual into the family, the work group, and even the community. Thus, psychological crisis can become a public health challenge by virtue of its ability to reach far beyond the individual who initially experiences the crisis. Perhaps the most severe and disabling crisis contexts would be large scale disasters and, of course, psychological trauma, whether as a result of disasters or individual experience, such as sexual or physical assault. It has been argued that psychological trauma can leave in its wake the most severe and disabling of the adult-onset mental disorders (Everly and Lating, 2004).

MENTAL HEALTH CONSEQUENCES

What is the magnitude of risk for experiencing a significant critical incident or trauma that might yield a crisis or some otherwise significantly adverse impact upon one's mental and/or spiritual health? What are the mental health consequences of such exposure?

- Evidence suggests over 60% of adults in the United States will be exposed to a traumatic event during their lifetime (Breslau et at., 1998).
- The rate of trauma exposure for children and adolescents has been estimated to be about 40% (see Ford, Ruzek, & Niles, 1996).
- The conditional risk of developing posttraumatic stress disorder (PTSD) was found to be 13% for females and 6% for males in a general community sample (Breslau et al., 1998).
- Suicide rates have been seen to increase 62% in the first year after an earthquake, increase 31% in the first two years after a hurricane, and increase by almost 14% four years after a flood (Krug et at., 1998).
- The prevalence of PTSD was found to be 13% in a sample

of suburban law enforcement officers (Robinson, Sigman, & Wilson, 1997).

- The prevalence of posttraumatic stress disorder ranged from 15% to 31% for samples of urban firefighters based on a traumatic exposure prevalence ranging from 85% to 91% (Beaton, Murphy, & Corneil, 1996).

- According to a national poll conducted by the American Red Cross (ARC, 2001) from October 5 to 8, 2001, 20% of the American public reported significant psychological symptoms related to the terrorist attacks of 2001.

- In the Fall of 1991, what was at that time the deadliest shooting in U.S. history occurred in Kileen, Texas (North et al., 1994). North and her colleagues (North et al., 2002a) followed the longitudinal course of this event from a psychiatric perspective. The rates of PTSD, major depression, and panic at the 6-8 week baseline for a sample of 136 were 28.8%, 10.3%, and 2.3%, respectively. At the one year follow-up (n=124), those rates were 17.7%, 4.9%, and 2.4%, respectively. There were no cases of delayed onset PTSD. Overall recovery from PTSD at the 3 year assessment was about 50%.

- Subsequent to the September 11, 2001 terrorist attacks on the World Trade Center, during the period from October 11 through December, 2001, the CDC Behavioral Risk Factor Surveillance System (BRFSS) initiative sampled 3,512 adult residents of Connecticut, New Jersey, and New York via a random digit dialed telephone survey. The "results of the survey suggest a widespread psychological and emotional impact in all segments of the three states' populations" (CDC, 2002, p.784) Seventy-five percent of respondents reported having problems attributed to the attacks: 48% of respondents reported that they experienced anger after the attacks, 37.5%

reported worry, 23.9% reported nervousness, and 14.2% reported sleep disturbance. About 12% of respondents reported receiving help, but the majority of the help received was from family members and friends.

- Galea, Ahern, et al. (2002) assessed the prevalence of acute posttraumatic stress disorder (PTSD) and depression among residents of Manhattan five to eight weeks after the terrorist attacks of September 11. Among those interviewed, 7.5% reported symptoms consistent with a diagnosis of current PTSD related to the attacks and 9.7% reported symptoms consistent with depression occurring within the previous 30 days. Among respondents who lived closer to Ground Zero, south of Canal, the prevalence of PTSD was 20%.

- Subsequent to another terrorist attack on American soil, North and colleagues (1999) assessed the prevalence of psychiatric disorders amongst a cohort of 255 survivors of the Oklahoma City bombing at 6 months post-event. Results indicated that 45% of the subjects possessed a psychiatric disorder. The authors report the onset of symptoms was rapid (76% reporting same day onset).

CLINICAL SYNDROMES AND THE CRISIS TRIAD

Earlier we defined crisis as a disequilibrium, that is, a disruption of the "steady state" of psychological processing that the mind fights to maintain. When faced with minor challenges or daily frustrations, the mind employs various compensatory mechanisms. Commonly used compensatory mechanisms might include denial of the problem, rationalization, intellectualization, creation of a psychological protective shell, and/or problem solving techniques. Some of these compensation mechanisms are obviously more constructive in the long-term than are others. Nevertheless, they all work to quickly reestablish a psychological equilibrium in the face of a perturbation. Crises arise when the coping, or compensatory, mechanisms one usually employs prove ineffectual. Thus, the perceived challenge cannot be resolved to the satisfaction of the person experiencing the crisis. It is during such periods as these that symptoms of decompensation begin to manifest themselves. Decompensation results when the individual cannot cope with a crisis condition and therefore cannot reestablish psychological homeostasis.

Decompensation - a breakdown in psychological equilibrium evidenced by a potentially wide and diverse collection of psychological symptoms of distress, maladaptive behavior patterns, and/or functional impairment.

The following represents a partial list of the most common crisis-related psychological and behavioral presentations that are sometimes thought of as decompensation patterns or symptoms.

The "Crisis Triad"

Perhaps the most common constellation of crisis reactions may be three co-varying reactions that may be referred to as the "crisis triad." The "crisis triad" consists of

- tendencies for behavioral impulsivity;
- diminished cognitive capabilities (insight, recall, problem-solving), but most importantly a diminished ability to understand the consequences of one's actions; and,
- an acute loss of future orientation, or a feeling of helplessness.

The crisis triad is not only common, it may be a latent syndrome in the majority of clinical presentations reviewed herein.

Other crisis syndromes may consist partially or wholly of the following reactions.

Panic

A panic attack is best thought of as a discrete paroxysmal interval of intense fear, psychological discomfort, and extreme psychophysiological arousal.

Psychological/behavioral symptoms of panic often include
- the belief that one is dying,
- extreme fear,
- uncertainty,
- hopelessness,
- a sense of acute environmental constriction, and/or
- possible phobia formation.

Physiological symptoms can be diverse and remarkably varied between individuals. They may include, but not be limited to
- sweating,
- cardiac palpitations,
- tachycardia (heart rate in excess of 100 beats per minute),
- bradycardia (heart rate less than 60 beats per minute),
- nausea,
- vertigo,
- hyperventilation.

Depression

Depression is not a single monolithic disorder, but rather represents a spectrum of symptom conditions. We are obviously most concerned with the more severe pole of the depression continuum. The primary psychological symptoms of depression include
- depressed mood,
- anhedonia,
- hopelessness, and
- suicidal ideation.

The classic physical symptoms of depression include
- loss of appetite,
- weight loss potential,

- diminished libido,
- terminal insomnia (sleep maintenance insomnia),
- psychomotor retardation, and
- diminished energy.

Hypomania

While hypomania may appear similar to anxiety, it is different. Hypomania represents a discrete period of several days, characterized by irritable or elevated mood. More specifically, individuals may exhibit

- a decreased need for sleep (2 - 3 hours of sleep);
- a rapid flow of ideas, rapid talkativeness;
- an inflated sense of self; and/or
- grandiosity, or perhaps even paranoid-like ideation.

Some hypomanic episodes may include extremely impulsive buying, gambling, or sexual behavior. Some individuals may attempt some form of self-medication to compensate for this conddition. Alcohol and other central nervous system depressants are commonly used.

Somatoform Conversion Reactions

The conversion variation of the somatoform disorder (physical symptoms without organic etiology) is typified by deficits in the motor and/or sensory systems. Psychological factors are the cause of or major augmenting factor in this array of physical dysfunctions which cannot be explained on the basis of organic pathophysiologic processes alone. Examples of conversion disorders would be

- conversion blindness,
- paralysis,
- mutism,
- deafness, and
- great difficulty swallowing.

Historically these disorders were referred to as "hysterical" disorders.

Acute Stress Disorder (ASD)

This diagnostic category was first officially introduced by the American Psychiatric Association in 1994. It is considered to be an anxiety disorder that lasts for a minimum of two days and a maximum of four weeks. The initiation of the symptoms must occur within four weeks of a traumatic event. The symptoms may include symptoms such as

- depersonalization, derealization, and numbing;
- recollective ideation of the traumatic event such as dreams, flashbacks, or recurrent thoughts/images of the traumatic event;
- avoidance of people, places, or things associated with the trauma; and
- symptoms of anxiety and autonomic nervous system hyperarousal.

Obviously the manifest symptom spectrum may vary markedly from person to person.

Posttraumatic Stress Disorder (PTSD)

This diagnostic category was first officially introduced in the Diagnostic and Statistical Manual of Mental Disorders, Third Edition (APA, 1980). The 1994 revision of that diagnostic taxonomy indicates that PTSD is a rather predictable sequelae of symptoms which lie in the wake of psychological trauma. Its key features include three symptom clusters subsequent to the exposure to a traumatic event.

- Intrusive memories and recollections of the traumatic event in the form of persistent and distressing dreams, flashbacks, and/or intrusive thoughts/images.

- Persistent avoidance of and withdrawal from people, places, and/or things associated with the traumatic event, as well as depressive symptoms.
- Persistent symptoms of increased arousal, such as hyperstartle reactions, irritability, angry outbursts, and sleep disturbance.

The diagnosis of PTSD does not overlap with ASD; therefore, this diagnosis cannot be made until the symptom duration has been at least one month. The delayed variant of PTSD is characterized by a symptom latency period of at least six months after the traumatic event.

Everly (Everly & Lating, 1995; 2004) has analyzed the posttraumatic stress disorder construct and found it to reveal two key components or constituents:

- neurologic hypersensitivity and
- psychologic hypersensitivity (Everly, 1993).

The neurologic hypersensitivity is thought to consist of a lowered depolarization threshold within the amygdaloid posterior hypothalamic efferent pathways of the limbic system, as well as other limbic-related structures such as the anterior pituitary. This functional hypersensitivity is thought to give rise to a potential over-reactive cascade of systemic hormonal phenomena, as well as behavioral impulsivity, irritability, and propensity for violence. The limbic hypersensitivity itself appears to result from

- an excess of excitatory neurotransmitters,
- a paucity of inhibitory neurotransmitters, and/or
- actual changes in dendritic receptor structures caused by chemical or genetic alterations (Everly, 1993).

The psychologic hypersensitivity is thought to arise from a violation of some deeply held belief. This belief is referred to as a worldview, or "Weltanschauung." Thus, a traumatic event, according to this perspective, is predicated upon some situation that violates a deeply-held and important worldview. Most commonly, we think of the traumatic event being a life threatening event - thus a violation to the assumption of safety discussed by writers such as Maslow (1970). Everly and Lating (2004) have identified five themes that seem universally traumatogenetic:

- Violation of the belief that the world is "just" or "fair." Thus, "Why would an infant die in a motor vehicle accident?"
- Violation of a sense of who you are by having not done something you should, or by having done something you should not have done.
- Abandonment, betrayal, violation of trust.
- Violation of a sense of safety, universally speaking.
- Disconfirmation of some core foundational belief about the nature of life itself, e.g., philosophy, science, spirituality, religion.

Figure 3.1 represents a model of PTSD. A review of Figure 3.1 reveals that the sine qua non of PTSD is a qualifying traumatic event. However, it also indicates that the interpretation, or meaning, that the individual assigns to the event greatly affects the manifest severity of the subsequent symptoms. This in no way should be misinterpreted to lead to a "blame the victim" conclusion. Figure 3.2 attempts to address this issue by indicating that while interpretation of the traumatic event is an important aspect of the PTSD picture, traumatic events, in and of themselves, carry a certain degree of inherent potency (see Figure 3.2).

Grief/Bereavement Reactions

Grief and bereavement are normal reactions to loss. These reactions become pathognomonic (characteristic of disease) when their intensity and/or chronicity become excessive - that is, unusually debilitating to

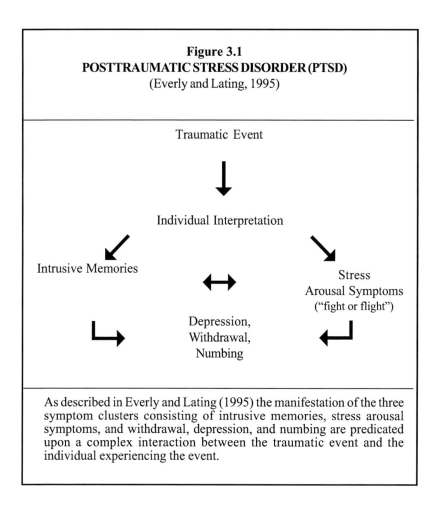

Figure 3.1
POSTTRAUMATIC STRESS DISORDER (PTSD)
(Everly and Lating, 1995)

Traumatic Event

Individual Interpretation

Intrusive Memories

Stress
Arousal Symptoms
("fight or flight")

Depression,
Withdrawal,
Numbing

As described in Everly and Lating (1995) the manifestation of the three symptom clusters consisting of intrusive memories, stress arousal symptoms, and withdrawal, depression, and numbing are predicated upon a complex interaction between the traumatic event and the individual experiencing the event.

one's life. Many current formulations argue that grief and bereavement reactions are, by definition, pathognomonic when they satisfy the diagnostic criteria for a major depressive episode. Generally speaking, it may be suggested that normal grief reactions will not include extreme guilt reactions, feelings of worthlessness, or psychomotor retardation. Further, the vast majority of individuals cope successfully with loss by a repetitive process of remembrance and analysis known as "working through," or a constructive compartmentalization process.

Figure 3.2
SUBJECTIVE INTERPRETATION AND EVENT POTENCY

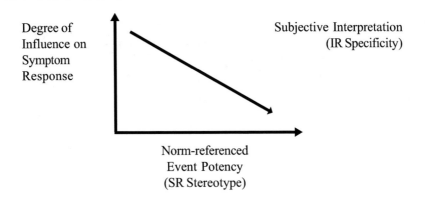

Degree of
Influence on
Symptom
Response

Subjective Interpretation
(IR Specificity)

Norm-referenced
Event Potency
(SR Stereotype)

Psychophysiological Disorders

Psychophysiological disorders may be thought of as stress-related physiologic disorders related to crisis or trauma. Unlike the diagnosis of somatoform conversion reactions where there is no clear-cut pathophysiologic mechanism, the psychophysiologic disorder has a relatively well understood mechanism of pathophysiology. While the somatoform conversion reaction only affects the sensory or motor systems, the psychophysiologic disorder can affect any system in the human body (see Everly & Lating, 2004 for a review of the physiology of stress response mechanisms). Psychophysiologic disorders not only represent medical conditions caused by extreme stress, but also include medical conditions exacerbated by extreme stress.

Brief Reactive Psychosis

In rare instances a crisis or traumatic stressor may be of such intensity as to cause a brief psychotic episode. The symptoms of such a reaction would include either delusions, hallucinations, disorganized/ incoherent speech, and/or disorganized, bizarre, or catatonic behavior. The duration of such a reactive episode is at least one day but is less than one month, according to the American Psychiatric Association's diagnostic nosology (classification; APA, 1994).

Obsessive-Compulsive Disorders

A crisis, as noted early, engenders a process of decompensation. Some individuals, in an attempt to recompensate, demonstrate obsessive and/or compulsive symptom patterns. Such symptom patterns may include repetitive and persistent thoughts (obsessions) and/or repetitive behaviors, or the unrealistically rigid adherence to rules, rituals, and routines (compulsions).

Other Crisis-related Symptoms

In addition to the aforementioned crisis-related symptom patterns, there exist several other significant maladaptive responses to crisis. Anger and violence appear to be on the rise as maladaptive responses to crisis. In their most extreme form, these reactions may lead to homicidal ideation, gestures, and actual acts.

Violence may be directed toward oneself, e.g., suicide, or toward others. Violence is clearly a maladaptive coping response to crisis. For many, suicide represents a "permanent solution" to what is often a temporary problem. And even then, the "solution" is not without a significant legacy of pain and problems for the friends and family members of the deceased. Violence toward others has lasting implications both psychosocial and legal. From the crisis interventionists' perspective, violence is reason for immediate facilitation of access to continued care.

PSYCHOLOGICAL TRIAGE

Effective crisis intervention must certainly be predicated upon effective psychological triage. How do we ascertain who most needs assistance? How do we reduce the chances that we may inadvertently interfere with normal symptom manifestations and the natural recovery process? This is the essence of psychological triage.

To underestimate the severity of a victim's crisis state may lead to a career-threatening, marriage-threatening, or even life-threatening condition. But, to overestimate the severity, to respond too aggressively, thereby interfering with natural recovery mechanisms, may also lead to adverse consequences. While there is no crystal ball that allows us to precisely predict who will be most in need of subsequent assistance, there are both empirical and conceptual guidelines that may be of assistance in the process of triage in the midst of a psychological crisis. Not every person exposed to a traumatic, or critical, incident will need subsequent psychological support from the mental health community. The fact is that most individuals possess natural recovery mechanisms that will prove quite adequate in most times of catastrophe, whether personal or communal (NIMH, 2002; Everly & Mitchell, 1999). Remember, while virtually 100% of persons directly exposed to a traumatic event will experience some degree of distress, somewhere between 9% and 45% of persons exposed may develop significant dysfunction, based upon approximations of PTSD. Overly aggressive crisis intervention may interfere with the natural recovery mechanisms of those very individuals whom we seek to assist (NIMH, 2002; Dyregrov, 1999). Inappropriate intervention could also further jeopardize the well-being of the victim through engendering self-doubt or imposing an undesirable stigma.

To assist in the determination of when to intervene, the notion of psychological triage seems worthy of discussion.

THE A-B-C PRINCIPLE OF TRIAGE

Alan Lakein (1973) authored an influential book on time management. In that text he argued that the preservation of resources is essential and that time is the essential resource. He noted that the demands upon our time come in three categories: A, B, and C.

A = Important & Urgent

B = Important but not Urgent, or Urgent but not Important

C = Neither Important nor Urgent

He then suggests that we should attend only to the As in our lives. The mistake that most people make is to attend to Bs. He says that Bs are demands in transition. Most Bs become Cs. Those Bs that become As then warrant attention. To attend to all Bs is to waste time and resources on demands that will take care of themselves.

Lakein's model can be converted to psychological triage wherein:

A = Highly dysfunctional

B = Distressed (increased stress, possible acute dysfunction that resolves with respite)

C = Functional, sometimes heroic

From this perspective, the interventionist should directly attend to As, monitor Bs, and leave Cs alone. In situations that are not acutely life threatening, the passage of time is usually helpful in de-escalating a volatile situation and in eroding symptoms of distress.

Recognizing the A

- The best predictors of posttraumatic stress disorder (PTSD) appear to be the following peritraumatic (occurring during or shortly after a critical incident) reactions:
  - dissociation (estrangement from self; estrangement from environment),
  - intense depressive symptoms, "giving up,"
  - psychogenic amnesia,
  - syncope (fainting),
  - dysfunctional symptoms of parasympathetic nervous system activity, and
  - malignant symptoms of sympathetic nervous system activity, e.g., panic attacks and sustained elevated heart

rate that does not attenuate even under non-threatening environmental conditions (see Everly, 1999 for a review).

- Other symptoms that require attention are
  - expression of suicidal and/or homicidal inclinations,
  - evidence of self-medication,
  - expression of violent behavior and/or inclinations,
  - severe guilt reactions, including "survivor guilt,"
  - expressions of helplessness, hopelessness,
  - vegetative depressive symptoms,
  - neuromuscular immobility, freezing,
  - severe dysfunctional time distortion, and
  - brief psychotic reactions (see Everly, 1999; Watson & Shalev, 2005 for reviews).

Finally, the restoration of normal sleep patterns, cessation of dissociative symptoms, and the restoration of a normal startle response may be among the best indicators of "recovery" from a traumatic incident.

SUMMARY

While clearly there is a vast array of crisis related symptoms, we have enumerated some of the most common that the crisis interventionist is likely to encounter.

The brief summaries provided in this chapter are not intended to be formal diagnostic guidelines, but rather to be merely a guide to generating a working hypotheses during a crisis situation. Formal diagnosis is typically the domain of the clinician working outside of the crisis venue with the aid of the opportunity to conduct a clinical interview, complete mental status exam, psychiatric history, and psychological testing protocols.

PART TWO

Integrative Intervention

C H A P T E R   F O U R

The National Incident Management System (NIMS)

"The quality of an organization can never exceed the quality of the minds that make it up."- Harold R. McAlindon

The effectiveness of a particular crisis or disaster intervention often relies on the organization behind the crisis response. Haphazard, unplanned, uncoordinated, and poorly designed intervention services are generally ineffective and, at times, they may even be counterproductive. The disaster response to Hurricane Katrina stands as a tragic reminder of the consequences of failed leadership and failed coordination of services. From the very inception of a crisis or disaster response, mental health providers and other intervention personnel must combine many skills and consider a wide range of important factors before beginning an intervention. Psychological crisis intervention personnel must blend their assessment skills with strategic planning skills and the selection of the best available crisis intervention procedures to match the needs of the people who are in a state of crisis. We shall discuss this notion in far greater depth later in this and other chapters.

The need for an organized and highly coordinated disaster response extends to mental health services as well as all other services. If services are to be truly integrative, there must be a continuum of mental health services, and those services must be fully incorporated into the provision of all other services.

Crisis interventionists must always answer the traditional questions – *who, what, when, where, and why*. That is, they need to know who needs support, what types of assistance they need, when they need the support, where the support personnel will apply the crisis intervention services, and why the support is required.

The greater the scale of the incident and the more complex the situation producing the crisis, the greater is the need for organization. Disaster-focused crisis intervention work, for example, requires an elaborate network of interrelated elements to deliver the best support services, at the right times, and under the best circumstances to assure the greatest potential for an effective and efficient crisis response. That response requires logistical support and coordination. Housing, transportation, communications, security, food and water, supplies, liaison with other organizations, and the replacement and rehabilitation of fatigued personnel are all elements of logistical support and coordination functions in a large scale incident.

A mental health response to large-scale events, such as terrorist attacks, biological threats, chemical hazards, and natural and technological disasters, does not occur in a vacuum. Instead, large-scale events generate impressive official and unofficial responses from a plethora of agencies, organizations, and resources. Crisis intervention resources from the National Voluntary Organizations Active in Disaster (NVOAD), such as the International Critical Incident Stress Foundation, the National Organization of Victim Assistance, the American Red Cross, the Salvation Army, and numerous other organizations, including faith-based programs, will be called upon to assist disaster-impacted communities. All of the crisis intervention organizations must work together for the common good; and they must be careful not to interfere with the many other resources, such as fire services, search and rescue, law enforcement, and the National Guard, who are working at a disaster. The crisis intervention aspects of a disaster response are only one component of the overall operation. They will need to coordinate and cooperate with every other component of the disaster relief network. All intervention teams must also recognize that they ultimately function under the direction of an incident commander or incident manager while they are engaged in support work at a large-scale event.

Even before the 2001 terrorist attacks on the United States, the federal government, in cooperation and collaboration with law enforcement and emergency response organizations, was engaged in the development of a nationwide comprehensive program to manage emergency operations. The need for such a program obviously became more evident after the attacks. The program is entitled the **National Incident Management System (NIMS)**. The NIMS program includes the **Incident Command System (ICS)**, which itself is the result of extensive development efforts dating back to the organization of military operations as long ago as the American Civil War (1861-1864). Much of the current material on the ICS is the result of a nearly 40-year development process in emergency services organizations that began with a series of disastrous fires in California in 1970 (National Wildfire Coordinating Group, 1994).

This chapter will familiarize the reader with an overview of NIMS and its primary components, especially the Incident Command System (ICS). The coverage of NIMS and the ICS in this chapter, however, does not in any way constitute formal training in NIMS. The reader should view the material only as an overview and be cognizant of the fact that one must obtain appropriate training from an official US government source such as FEMA-NIMS@dhs.gov or http://www.fema.gov/emergency/nims/nims_training.shtm. The federal government has endorsed some states, tribal councils, counties, and emergency services organizations to provide NIMS training programs. All NIMS training, however, must adhere strictly to the training curriculum established by Federal Emergency Management Agency (NIMS Integration Center, 2007a, 2007b, 2007c).

ESSENTIAL INFORMATION

The *National Incident Management System* (NIMS) is an administrative system for the handling of any emergency, including the multi-jurisdictional and multi-agency response of local, state, and federal government resources to a large-scale incident such as a disaster. NIMS was specifically developed to enhance the capabilities of emergency responders from different jurisdictions and disciplines for working together more efficiently during natural disasters and other emergencies, including acts of terrorism. The NIMS approach to emergency management is one of standardization. It focuses on an incident management program with a set of commonly accepted emergency management structures and procedures, universal terminology, and inter-agency communication, cooperation, and mutual aid. NIMS places considerable emphasis on preparing for emergencies as well as on resource management during the response aspects of a disaster.

On February 28, 2003, the President of the United States issued Homeland Security Presidential Directive–5 (HSPD–5), *Management of Domestic Incidents* (Bush, 2003). This document directed the Secretary of Homeland Security to develop and administer a National Incident Management System (NIMS). The system assists communities in preparing for, responding to, and recovering from domestic events. It incorporates the best emergency management practices that have evolved over decades of experience. HSPD-5 requires all federal agencies to utilize the NIMS program in their prevention, mitigation, response, and recovery activities. Additionally, any local, tribal, state, or private organizations receiving federal funds are required to use the NIMS program (US Department of Homeland Security, 2004).

Because of the HSPD-5, the utilization of the NIMS Incident Command System has grown so widespread and so well-accepted that every individual, from any type of organization that responds to any domestic disaster, must receive training in the NIMS program. In the very near future, everyone working at a disaster site, including people providing crisis intervention services, will be required to produce evidence of NIMS-Incident Command System training. The time has come for people providing crisis intervention services to become familiar with the NIMS program, to accept training in the system, and to utilize it when they are providing services (NIMS Integration Center, 2007b, 2007c).

NIMS COMPONENTS

The NIMS program is extensive. There are literally hundreds of documents, totaling many thousands of pages of material, that detail the system. For crisis intervention personnel, familiarity with all of that information would be unnecessary and, needless to say, a time-consuming, monumental task. The emphasis in this chapter will be on an overview of the NIMS program and a focus on the essential information for crisis intervention providers. To start, we will first provide a broad overview of NIMS. There are six main components of NIMS. They are:

Command and Management

- Incident Command System
- Multi-agency Coordination
- Public Information System

Preparedness

This component covers every aspect of emergency planning, education, preparation of resources, training of personnel, and efforts to mitigate or eliminate potential threats.

Resource Management

The focus of this component is the identification, description, listing, and credentialing of all types of resources that might respond to a disaster. Many of these resources are located in one jurisdiction and loaned to other jurisdictions during emergencies. The term for borrowing and loaning of resources between jurisdictions is "mutual aid."

Communications and Information Management

The fourth component of the NIMS addresses the necessity for standardization of intra- and inter-organizational communications, as well as standard record keeping and other information management procedures.

Supporting Technologies

NIMS encourages the development, adoption, and utilization of new technologies that enhance emergency management. It also encourages the use of interoperable communication devices that allow organizations to communicate easily with one another during emergencies.

Ongoing Management and Maintenance

NIMS is a dynamic system. It requires openness and flexibility to change. The system needs vigilant maintenance to make adaptations, assuring that it is capable of responding appropriately to changes in the emergency management environment. NIMS is constantly re-evaluated and improved by a management team at the NIMS Integration Center within the Federal Emergency Management Agency (NIMS Integration Center, 2007d).

WHY THE INCIDENT COMMAND SYSTEM?

The Incident Command System (ICS) is the part of the NIMS program that will have the greatest impact on crisis intervention personnel and, therefore, it will receive the most attention in this chapter. Interventionists need to understand and accept the ICS. Working within the system is a necessity for crisis intervention personnel not only because it is required by the presidential directive (Bush, 2003), but also because ICS is the universal emergency management approach currently utilized within the United States and many other nations. ICS also offers a proven and useful organizational tool for crisis support personnel who are dealing with large-scale events that can quickly overwhelm their resources. The system helps crisis intervention organizations to work as teams and to monitor their own personnel to avoid stretching individuals beyond reasonable capacities. Working within the ICS offers crisis intervention personnel organizational acceptance and management strengths that they could not achieve if they work only as individuals or as isolated organizations (FEMA, 2004).

KEY FEATURES OF ICS

Common Terminology

Common terminology allows many different types of organizations to communicate with each other and to work together for the best possible management of an emergency. The umbrella of common terminology covers organizational functions, resource descriptions and incident facilities. Crisis intervention teams should emulate the common terminology philosophy of the ICS program. Unfortunately, there is currently very little standardization of terms in the crisis intervention field. The result is confusion and misinformation (Mitchell, 2007).

Modular Organization

One of the most important features of the ICS is the use of modules in its organizational structure. Depending on the size and complexity of the emergency, an Incident Commander may add to the ICS or remove from the ICS any specific modules he or she deems necessary. It is also possible to subdivide any module, if necessary, to enhance management and coordination functions. The Incident Commander is responsible for the entire organizational structure during an emergency. Changes in the ICS occur as responders assess the needs of the situation under "real world" field conditions. As additional modules are required, the ICS organizational structure expands from the top downward.

For example, let us suppose that an Incident Commander (IC) is advised by his or her staff that operations personnel are having a difficult time emotionally because many child victims are involved in a large-scale incident. The IC then assigns a staff member, called a Liaison Officer (LO), to take on the responsibility of assuring that crisis intervention services are provided to emergency operations personnel. The Liaison Officer requests a mental health team, or perhaps a Critical Incident Stress Management (CISM) team, to come to the scene. The team leader, or CISM Specialist, in charge of the team, reports to the Liaison Officer who then assigns certain overall responsibilities for the emotional care of operations to the CISM specialist. The CISM Specialist subsequently assigns specific tasks to the members of the team and deploys them to carry out the tasks.

If necessary, the human services functions can expand. Suppose further assessment of the situation, described in the example above, indicates that the incident is also causing significant distress for large numbers of community people. The Liaison Officer could request that the CISM Specialist assign another individual as the CISM team leader in charge of the team's support of operations personnel, while a second team member is assigned to a team whose role is to assist the community members. Both team leaders would then report to the CISM Specialist who, in turn, would report to the Liaison Officer. Additional crisis intervention resources can be called to the scene if they are needed. However, every time the Incident Commander adds a significant new function to the ICS, there must be a commensurate increase in the size of the leadership corps (NIMS Integration Center, 2007d).

Management by Objective

In the ICS, specific, measurable objectives are established as early as possible. Everyone in the management structure is informed of the objectives and each part of the organization supports the achievement of the objectives. Another term for management by objectives is *strategic planning*.

Incident Action Plans

During each operational period an Incident Action Plan (IAP) must be developed. The IAP provides the objectives for both the operations and the support activities for that particular work period. An IAP, therefore, includes the proposed activities of the crisis intervention team for a specific work shift. IAPs help to answer the important *who, what, when, where, and why* questions mentioned earlier.

Span of Control

Within the ICS, leaders supervise between three and seven subordinates depending on the circumstances and the complexity of the situation. Most leaders in emergencies are overwhelmed by a span of control that is too large. More than seven subordinates is an excessive number. Crisis intervention specialists should select a few subordinate team leaders and subdivide the responsibilities for the situation's human services among them.

Facilities

Very early in a large-scale incident, the managers must identify locations and facilities that will sustain the operations and support services. The first facilities to be established are those for the command post and communications. A staging area is also essential. The staging area is a location where most of the responding resources check-in and remain until needed. It is very important to establish facilities for medical triage and treatment as well as for food services, supplies, and crisis intervention services.

Comprehensive Resource Management

All resources, equipment, teams, supplies, and facilities must be categorized, ordered, dispatched, and tracked during the incident. At the conclusion of the incident, all of the personnel and materials utilized during the incident must be recovered and restored to a "ready" condition. The crisis intervention team usually goes through a Post Action Staff Support program to assure that all team members are adequately recovered from the intense work of the deployment (Mitchell, 2007).

Integrated Communications

The ICS depends upon intra- and inter-organizational communications and a comprehensive plan for communications.

Clear Command Structure

The agency with primary jurisdictional authority designates the individual at the scene of an incident with the responsibility to *establish command immediately in the situation*. Provisions should also be in place to *transfer command* efficiently to higher-ranking authorities when they arrive on scene, or temporarily to a subordinate when the Incident Commander needs rest. Transfer procedures have typically been developed well in advance of an emergency and transitions of authority in the field usually appear seamless.

Chain of Command, Unity of Command, Unified Command

There are five important concepts that apply to ICS command issues. They are:

- Chain of Command
- Command Staff
- Command Post
- Unity of Command
- Unified Command

Chain of Command refers to the orderly line of authority over the incident operations. Simply put, team or unit members report to their team leaders. Team leaders report to division supervisors, who, in turn, report to branch directors. In the higher levels of the command structure, branch directors report to section chiefs who communicate to the Incident Command level within ICS. The chain of command helps maintain the span of control described earlier. Figure 4.1 provides an overview of the ICS system. It is especially helpful in clarifying the chain of command in ICS.

In the ICS the Incident Commander is in charge of the management of the incident. Reporting to the IC will be the section chiefs of major sections of the ICS. The four most common major sections of the ICS are: "Operations," "Planning," "Logistics," and "Finance/Administration." Below the major sections come branches. A branch covers a specific area of responsibility. For example, under "operations" there may be several branches. One might be "search," another could be "fire suppression," and another could be "helicopter operations." The number and types of branches may vary from incident to incident, depending on the magnitude of the event and the special requirements that might be encountered. In some cases, if it is not placed under the command staff working directly with the Incident Commander, crisis intervention services or a CISM team might be designated as a separate branch working under the operations chief.

Each branch can be subdivided into smaller areas of responsibility if the incident is very large and further operational areas are required. Note that every agency, organization, or special service at a disaster is known as a *resource* in the ICS. Crisis intervention teams and CISM teams are, therefore, considered a resource within the ICS. The smallest operating segment of the ICS system is referred to as a unit. On the right hand side of Figure 4.1 are the *key titles*. A leader commands a unit and reports to a supervisor who, in turn, reports to a branch director. A branch director reports to a section chief who finally reports to the Command level of the ICS. The command level of the ICS has a staff to assist the Incident Commander. Command Staff and the Incident Commander comprise the command level of the ICS.

The Incident Commander's *Command Staff* consists of at least a *Safety Officer* (SO), a *Liaison Officer* (LO), and *a Public Information Officer* (IO). In some situations it is necessary that the command staff also have a *Medical Advisor,* a *Security Advisor,* and a *Specialty Advisor* (e.g., a scientific advisor, hazardous materials, railroad, building collapse, or crisis intervention specialist). Other Command Staff positions may be added to address unusual circumstances. Remember that the span of control is important and Incident Commanders do not want more than seven people reporting to them. In fact, most ICs prefer only three to five staff officers to work with them as Command Staff in the command post.

The *Command Post* (CP) is the physical location near the scene in which the IC and the Command Staff make decisions and oversee all of the activities associated with the operations in the field. Command Posts may range from the extremely simple to the very complex, depending on the resources available within the primary jurisdiction. Some CPs are no more sophisticated than the hood or tailgate of a vehicle, while others are housed in elaborate, well-equipped buses or large trailers with communications consoles and a small conference room for Command Staff meetings.

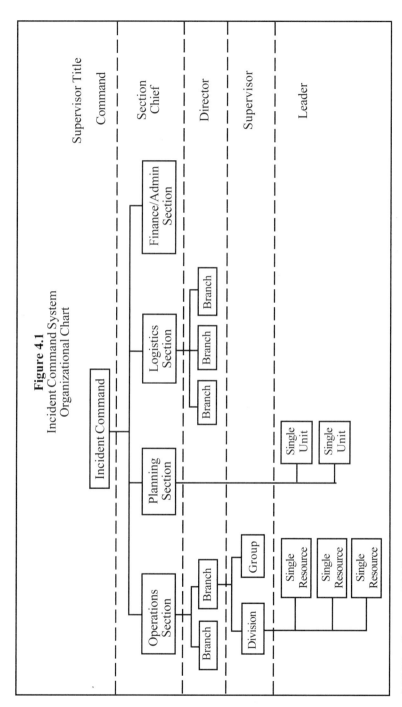

Figure 4.1
Incident Command System
Organizational Chart

(NIMS on line.com, 2004)

Unity of Command is the term used to describe the relationship between an individual and a supervisor. Every individual within the ICS has a designated supervisor. If a crisis intervention worker needs assistance from an individual at the scene of an emergency, only that individual's immediate supervisor could authorize the person to provide the assistance. Without unity of command in a large-scale incident such as a disaster, there would be enormous confusion at the scene.

Unified Command is a concept applied in large-scale events involving multiple agencies from either a single jurisdiction or a combination of agencies from multiple jurisdictions. Top leaders from each jurisdiction or agency meet together, develop a common strategic approach, and accept a single Unified Commander (UC) to lead the overall operations. In many cases, aspects of the Unified Command structure have been worked out in advance of a large-scale event. Unified Command enhances the ability of different agencies to work together without negatively affecting the authority, responsibility, and accountability of individuals and their organizations.

A terrorist event is a good example of a situation in which the concept of unified command is essential. In all terrorist events within the United States, the Federal Bureau of Investigation (FBI) becomes the lead agency (US Coast Guard, 2006). This has been established by Federal mandate in the aftermath of the September 11, 2001 attacks. Someone from the FBI is appointed the Incident Commander. All other agencies and their personnel then commit themselves to assist the IC in the management of the terrorist incident and the successful fulfillment of the strategy developed by the FBI.

PLACEMENT OF PSYCHOLOGICAL CRISIS INTERVENTION TEAMS IN ICS

For many years, discussions have occurred regarding the placement of psychological crisis intervention teams within the ICS. Some think they should be under operations support at the branch level. Others argue for placement in the logistics section within the Medical Unit. Still others argue for a placement in the command level of the ICS. Perhaps it might help to think of the Command Level as people- and relationship-oriented activities. However, every activity in the Planning and Liaison, Operations, Logistics, and Finance sections of the ICS are task-oriented. The United States Coast Guard made a decision to place the crisis intervention services in the command level. "Due to the importance of the mental well-being of all response personnel and the highly specialized nature of the program, the CISM Specialist would be assigned to the Command Level of the organization and Would Report Directly [*sic*]to the IC or UC" (United States Coast Guard, 2001, pg. 82). The practice of placing the CISM Specialist in the Command Staff is reaffirmed in the more recent publication of the *USCG Incident Management Handbook.* "…The CISM Specialist is normally assigned in Logistics under the Medical Unit Leader; however, an additional CISM Specialist is often assigned in the Command Staff working directly for the IC" (United States Coast Guard, 2006. pg. 82).

In the diagram below, the Command Function of the ICS system has been outlined with a sample command staff shown.

Figure 4.2
The Advisory Staff

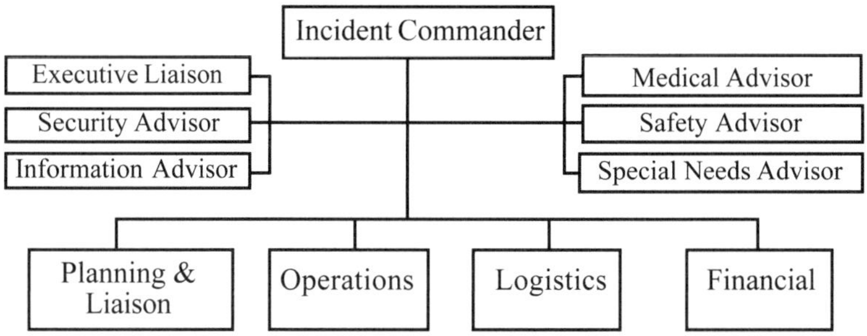

FUNCTIONAL AREAS IN THE INCIDENT COMMAND SYSTEM

The five main functions in ICS are the following:

- Command (to manage all aspects of the emergency response),
- Planning (to assess intelligence and develop Incident Action Plans),
- Operations (to apply tactics to carry out the Command's strategy),
- Logistics (to obtain and manage resources for the mission),
- and Finances (to maintain records, write reports, and handle administrative functions)

As described above, crisis intervention resources relate most closely to the Command function in ICS. The other four functions are extremely important and will be ongoing in an emergency, but crisis intervention personnel are not typically directly involved in managing or dealing with those functions. Any relationships they have with Planning, Operations, Logistics, and Finance are more cursory and are generally arranged by the Crisis Intervention Specialist who is working with the Command Liaison Officer.

Crisis intervention organizations would be wise to mirror some of the organizational structure and functions of the five ICS functions. The Crisis Intervention Specialist should have a crisis intervention liaison to relate to other organizations. It is important for a crisis intervention resource to have an administration specialist to keep records and write reports on the crisis team's activities. The administration specialist should also make the necessary arrangements to obtain the basic supplies and resources to support the crisis intervention team in the field. A crisis intervention team should have a planning section to develop crisis intervention action plans for each work shift.

Crisis teams must work with a single *Point of Contact* (POC) for all of the crisis intervention resources being brought to the scene. When dispatched to a scene, crisis intervention team leaders should be instructed that upon the team's arrival, the team leader should check in with the Liaison Officer from the Command Staff. More than likely that person will assign the team to the Crisis Intervention Specialist or CISM Specialist who will brief the resource and incorporate it into the Incident Action Plan. Deployment of specific crisis intervention resources are made by the Crisis Intervention Specialist. Of course, the types of crisis intervention resources must be matched to the needs of the people requiring assistance. All requests and requirements for additional resources should be communicated to the Crisis Intervention Specialist who then passes those requests on to the Command Liaison Officer. The Liaison Officer then asks the Logistics Chief to fulfill the requests and communicate back to the Liaison Officer the success or failure of obtaining the necessary resources on behalf of the crisis intervention team.

All crisis intervention contact with the Planning, Operations, Logistics, and Finance sections should always be coordinated and directed through the Crisis Intervention Specialist working in conjunction with the Command Liaison Officer. Adherence to such a policy will limit confusion and help to maintain an appropriate span of control and adherence to the resource management guidelines.

PRINCIPLES OF OPERATIONS IN LARGE-SCALE INCIDENTS

Certain principles form the foundation for effective and efficient crisis intervention services in an emergency. Every effort should be made to understand and adhere to these principles of operation.

1. Psychological crisis intervention personnel should not respond to an emergency unless they are requested by appropriate authorities. Crisis response personnel must be given instructions for arriving at the scene and reporting in with appropriate ICS personnel.

2. All crisis intervention personnel should be part of a recognized emergency response organization (unless an individual has been specifically requested to respond to the scene because of his or her specialized knowledge and skills). They should carry with them evidence of ICS training and copies of professional credentials and certificates indicating that they have received training in crisis intervention.

3. All crisis intervention teams should have a designated team leader who should report to the Command Liaison. The Command Liaison will assign the team to function under the direction of the Crisis Intervention Specialist or CISM Specialist during the emergency operation. Specialists are the most highly trained and experienced personnel from a particular resource. Some personnel are temporarily assigned to a specialist role until personnel with a greater breath and depth of knowledge and skill in a field can be brought to the scene.

4. All crisis intervention teams and other resources should be aware that they must **function within the Incident Command System** of the National Incident Management System.

5. Crisis intervention resources do not have the luxury of independent function in an emergency. They must work under the Incident Commander, be part of the Incident Action Plan, submit to resource management procedures, and respect the ICS principles such as line of command, span of control, and common terminology. In other words, they must be accountable to ICS authorities when working at an emergency.

6. Crisis intervention resources should respond to distress, impairment, or dysfunction, not just to the occurrence of an event.

7. Crisis intervention resources should not engage in psychotherapy, attempts to cure medical and psychological pathology, or any other activity that is beyond the confines of a supportive Critical Incident Stress Management, crisis intervention, or "psychological first aid" approach.

8. Crisis intervention resources should carefully assess the situation and its impact on the people involved. Keep in mind that most reactions to traumatic events do not turn into Posttraumatic Stress Disorder, yet people need support during emergencies. Once they have adequately assessed the situation and the severity of the impact on the personnel, the crisis intervention team should develop a crisis intervention strategy and select the most appropriate interventions to apply to those in need of support.

9. Crisis intervention services ought to be strategic in orientation and should match the needs of the people requiring assistance.

10. All crisis intervention services should be carefully timed to achieve the best possible outcomes. They should be organized to assist the right target populations, with the right types of interventions, at the best time, and by the most appropriate crisis intervention providers (Everly, 2000; Mitchell 2007).

SUMMARY

The Incident Command System is a well-developed and structured method of managing emergencies. It has a proven, 40-year record of accomplishment in emergency services organizations. ICS accepts crisis and disaster mental health intervention services as another important resource. With only minor alterations, psychological intervention resources can work easily within the system and provide their services to distressed people. In fact, the ICS system can facilitate the delivery of appropriate support services to operations personnel as well as to the citizens in need of support. Providers of disaster mental health services must be conversant in the ICS because it is the platform of delivery of such services.

CHAPTER FIVE

Integrative Crisis Intervention and Disaster Mental Health: The Critical Incident Stress Management (CISM) System

---

Psychological intervention subsequent to crises and even mass disasters has historically been characterized by reactive, event-centered practices. As noted in Chapter One, the crisis intervention movement itself has been a movement often conceptualized as an event-driven process with little appreciation for the variability inherent in the temporal trajectory of the human response to mass disasters. Univariate, or limited scope, crisis intervention models originated from community mental health initiatives (Parad, 1966; Parad & Parad, 1968; Langsley, Machotka, & Flomenhaft, 1971; Decker & Stubblebine, 1972), grief counseling (Lindemann, 1944), and community psychiatry movements (Caplan, 1961, 1964), as well as the "forward psychiatry" initiatives of the great world wars (Salmon, 1919; Artiss, 1963; Kardiner & Spiegel, 1947). More recent recommendations, however, have called for crisis intervention and disaster mental health services to be delivered in an integrated, multi-component format (Raphael, 1986; Everly & Mitchell, 1999; Ritchie, Friedman, Watson, Ursano, Wessely, & Flynn, 2004; US Dept of Heath & Human Services, 2004; Sheehan, Everly, & Langlieb, 2004; Ruzek, Young, Cordova, & Flynn, 2004; Paul & Blum, 2005; Boscarino, Adams, Foa, Landrigan, 2006; Kaminsky, McCabe, Langlieb, & Everly, 2005; 2007).

In this chapter, we shall examine Critical Incident Stress Management (CISM) as a strategic delivery platform for providing integrated and comprehensive multi-component psychological/behavioral services in the wake of critical incidents, large and small.

INTEGRATIVE PSYCHOTHERAPY

The development of an integrated, multi-component approach to critical incidents is not without precedent. The parallel of psychotherapy seems appropriate to review.

Historically, the field of psychotherapy appeared to evolve through three distinct phases: the univariate, the eclectic, and the integrative. The early years of psychotherapy were characterized by the practice of a multitude of diverse, univariate psychotherapeutic practices based upon singular theoretical orientations of psychopathology and healing, such as behavior therapy, person-centered psychotherapy, and psychoanalysis, to name a few. Rivalry among psychotherapeutic orientations has a long and undistinguished history.

Later, there seemed to be recognition that the aforementioned schools and their psychotherapeutic practices could co-exist, but not coincidentally. The eclectic phase saw the implementation of a singular intervention chosen from a collection of possible interventions, based upon a multitude of theoretical mechanisms of action. The selection of the intervention mechanism was based upon the clinician's assessment as to which intervention best suited the needs of the patient at that point in time.

Finally, the integrative approach to psychotherapy emerged. Integrative psychotherapy may be thought of as the implementation of an integrated array of psychotherapeutic interventions concurrently combined and catalytically sequenced in such a manner as to best respond to the unique needs, or "idiographic heterogeneity," of a given patient or group of patients. According to Millon, Grossman, Meagher,

Millon, and Everly (1999), "The palette of methods and techniques available to the therapist must be commensurate with the idiographic heterogeneity of the patient for whom the methods and techniques are intended" (1999, p. 145). Ultimately, such an approach to treatment formulation would lead the therapist to choose the best therapeutic intervention, or set of therapeutic interventions, to meet the needs of the patient at that present point in time. This, of course, is what Paul (1966) urged all therapists to do in his early work.

INTEGRATIVE CRISIS INTERVENTION AND DISASTER RESPONSE

The field of crisis intervention and disaster mental health response has evolved in a remarkably parallel fashion, progressing from univariate, to eclectic, to an integrative approach. The early years of critical incident response were characterized by the practice of a multitude of diverse, univariate intervention practices based upon singular theoretical orientations, such as behavioral crisis intervention, Critical Incident Stress Debriefing (CISD), multi-stressor debriefing, cognitive behavioral crisis intervention, specific models developed by the American Red Cross, the National Organization for Victims Assistance, the forward psychiatry military models emphasizing the PIE construct, and Roberts' crisis intervention approach, to name a few. Unfortunately, as with psychotherapeutic orientations, rivalry among critical incident response orientations has a long and undistinguished history.

And as with the psychotherapeutic orientations, there later seemed to be some minimal recognition that the aforementioned critical response orientations might co-exist, or exist with population specificity, but not coincidentally. This eclectic phase saw the implementation of a singular intervention chosen from a collection of possible interventions, based upon a multitude of theoretical mechanisms of action.

And finally the integrative approach to critical incident response emerged. Integrative psychological crisis intervention and disaster mental health response may be thought of as the implementation of an integrated array of critical incident interventions concurrently combined and catalytically sequenced in such a manner as to best respond to the unique needs, or "idiographic heterogeneity," of a given individual or population.

Just as Paul (1966), Millon, Grossman, Meagher, Millon, and Everly (1999), and others urged an integrative approach to psychotherapy, Raphael (1986), Everly and Mitchell (1999), Ritchie, Friedman, Watson, Ursano, Wessely, and Flynn (2004), Ruzek, Young, Cordova, Flynn (2004), Everly and Langlieb (2003), Flannery and Everly (2004), and Watson and Shalev, (2005) urged an integrative approach to psychological crisis and disaster mental health intervention. As adapted from Millon, Grossman, Meagher, Millon, and Everly (1999), "The palette of methods and techniques available to the [interventionist] must be commensurate with the idiographic heterogeneity of the [individual] for whom the methods and techniques are intended" (1999, p. 145). Ultimately, as we stated in Chapter One, such an approach to treatment formulation would lead the interventionist to choose the best intervention, or set of interventions, to meet the needs of the individual at that present point in time.

Building upon those historical foundations, we see an integrative approach, both strategically and tactically, as an integrated multi-faceted system incorporating a full continuum of care. Critical Incident Stress Management (CISM), as a variation on the theme of integrative intervention, is consistent with Millon's concepts of potentiating pairings (using interacting combinations of interventions to achieve an enhancing clinical effect), catalytic sequences (sequentially combining tactical interventions in their most clinically useful ways), and polythetic selection (selecting the tactical interventions based on the specific needs of each situation). The various combinations and permutations that are actually utilized will be determined by the unique demands of each critical incident or disaster, and the unique demands of each target population, as they uniquely arise.

Ideally, this continuum of psychological care must be seamlessly integrated with a continuum of emergency medical services. As Ruzek and colleagues (2004) note, "Because much of the potential harm to survivors of disaster or terrorism (and their families) will be related to their mental health and role functioning, preparedness requires the active integration of behavioral health into emergency medicine in every component of disaster response...Delivery of direct mental health care must include: (1) survivor and family education; (2) identification and referral of those requiring immediate care and follow-up; (3) group education and support services; and (4) individual counseling. In order for effective response to occur, the integration of psychosocial care into disaster response must occur prior to the disaster itself, and will depend on effective collaboration between medical and mental health care providers. At workplaces, emergency medical care centers must ensure that staff and their families are properly trained and supported with regard to their disaster functions and encouraged to develop personal/family disaster plans" (p. 46).

According to Watson and Shalev (2005), "Early intervention in mass traumatic events should be embedded within a multidisciplinary, multi-tiered disaster mental health system. Early interventions should be utilized in a culturally sensitive manner, related to the local formulation of problems and ways of coping, and applied flexibly, in ways that match needs and situational context and take into account the ongoing stressors, reactions, and resources" (p. 123).

These then are the conceptual platforms for the integrative crisis intervention and disaster mental health approach prescribed in this volume.

RESISTANCE, RESILIENCE, RECOVERY: THE JOHNS HOPKINS MODEL

Before examining specific tactical formulations, let us examine a unique perspective on the continuum of care. The Johns Hopkins Perspectives Model of Disaster Mental Health (Kaminsky, McCabe, Langlieb, & Everly, 2005; 2007) employs a resistance, resilience, and recovery construct as a basic framework for organizing an integrative approach to disaster mental health. We shall briefly describe the fundamental characteristics of this outcome-driven approach, while mentioning psychological and sociological interventions that might be suited to enhance each.

Resistance

In the present context, the term **resistance** refers to the ability of an individual, group, organization, or entire population not to exhibit manifestations of clinical distress, impairment, or dysfunction that might otherwise be anticipated with critical incidents, terrorism, and even mass disasters. Resistance may be thought of as a form of psychological or behavioral immunity to distress and dysfunction.

Historically, this element of disaster mental health response was conspicuous in its absence. The notion of creating resistance represents a proactive step in emergency mental health. The introduction of this intervention to the pre-incident phase of the temporal continuum invites comparisons with the concepts of *psychological immunization* and *psychological body armor*.

According to Kaminsky and colleagues (2007), resistance can be developed via expectance and experience. More specifically, resistance can be developed via the following empirically supported, quadratic formulation, "expectancy and experience:"

- *Providing realistic preparation.* Setting appropriate expectations, developing stress management and coping skills, and providing realistic pre-incident training may all serve to foster stress resistance.

- *Fostering group cohesion and social support.* Social support has been shown to buffer stress (Flannery, 1990). The creation of group cohesion, with an underlying infrastructure for social support, may be useful (American Psychological Association, 2003). An essential element of fostering cohesion and support, we believe, will be effective crisis leadership and risk communications. Risk communication should be designed to provide the following five essential elements: information (and rumor deterrence), reassurance, direction, motivation, and a sense of connectedness.

- *Fostering positive cognitions.* Cognitive appraisals appear to be key determinants of stress (see Everly & Lating, 2002, for a review) and trauma (Ehlers & Clark, 2003). Positive cognitions may include cognitive reframing, positive memories of those lost, and/or identification with a noble motive, such as religion or nationalism.

- *Building self-efficacy and hardiness.* Building self-efficacy and hardiness is important to enhancing resistance to stress and fostering resilience. The primary formulation which will serve as the basis for this notion resides in the work of Albert Bandura (self-efficacy) and Kobasa, Maddi & Kahn (hardiness). *Self-efficacy:* Bandura's work is summarized in his magnum opus on self-efficacy and human agency (1997). Bandura defines the perception of self-efficacy as the belief in one's ability to organize and execute the courses of action required to achieve necessary and desired goals. This perception of control, or influence, Bandura points out, is an essential aspect of life itself; "People guide their lives by their beliefs of personal efficacy" (Bandura, 1997, p. 3). He goes on to note:

"People' s beliefs in their efficacy have diverse effects. Such beliefs influence the courses of action people choose to pursue, how much effort they put forth in given endeavors, how long they will persevere in the face of obstacles and failures, their resilience to adversity, whether their thought patterns are self-hindering or self-aiding, how much stress and depression they experience in coping with taxing environmental demands, and the level of accomplishments they realize" (Bandura, 1997, p.3).

- *Hardiness* (Kobasa, Maddi, & Kahn, 1982) is believed to be an insulating factor against stressors and may be considered another useful explanatory construct herein. Hardiness is characterized by the belief in one's own self-efficacy, i.e., the ability to exert control over relevant life events; the tendency to see stressful events as "challenges" to be overcome; and a strong commitment and sense of purpose.

Thus, the first goal of the Johns Hopkins Perspectives Model of Disaster Mental Health would be to build resistance. Mechanisms by which resistance may be created include the following:

- Perception of credible and competent leadership,
- Anticipatory guidance, setting appropriate expectations,
- Realistic training,
- Identification with a common purpose or goal,
- Identification with a higher ideal,
- Identification with a group, fostering of group identity,
- Fostering impact- and acute-phase task orientations,
- Stress management training,
- Provision of family support, as indicated, and
- Cognitive reframing.

Resilience

In the present context, the term **resilience** refers to the ability of an individual, group, organization, or entire population to rebound rapidly and effectively from psychological or behavioral disturbances associated with critical incidents, terrorism, or mass disasters.

The second goal of the Johns Hopkins Perspectives Model of Disaster Mental Health would be to enhance the resilience of targeted personnel. Processes by which resilience may be enhanced include the following:

- Surveillance and assessment of need,
- Effective leadership,
- A credible, accurate information flow (effective risk communication tactics, e.g., use of mass media, town meetings, briefings, etc.),
- Stress management,
- Establishment and utilization of social support networks,
- The fostering of an acute phase task orientation,
- Implementation of "psychological first aid,"
- More intensive crisis intervention (up to three contacts),
- Utilization of small group crisis intervention for naturally occurring cohorts and families,
- Pastoral crisis intervention and chaplaincy services, and
- Psychological triage.

Recovery

Finally, the term **recovery** refers to the ability of an individual, group, organization, or entire population to recover the ability to function adaptively - emotionally, mentally, and behaviorally - in the wake of significant clinical distress, impairment, or dysfunction subsequent to a critical incident, terrorist event, or mass disaster. The final goal of the Johns Hopkins Perspectives Model of Disaster Mental Health would be to serve as a platform for facilitating access to continued support and clinical services such as cognitive-behavioral therapeutic services, psychotropic medications, and rehabilitation (see Kaminsky, McCabe, Langlieb, & Everly, 2007).The Hopkins construction is a useful outcome-driven tool to assist in overarching strategic planning. We will discuss strategic and tactical planning in greater detail in a later chapter.

THE INTEGRATIVE CRITICAL INCIDENT STRESS MANAGEMENT (CISM) SYSTEM: CORE ELEMENTS

The Critical Incident Stress Management (CISM) strategic system for the formulation and delivery of crisis and disaster mental health services is consistent with the tripartite Johns Hopkins' formulation.

CISM represents, both strategically and tactically, an integrated, multi-faceted approach to crisis intervention and disaster response. Consistent with Theodore Millon's (Millon, Grossman, Meagher, Millon, & Everly, 1999) integrative concepts, the CISM approach has a *polythetic combinatorial nature* (selecting the tactical interventions as determined by the specific needs of each crisis situation) wherein specific crisis interventions within the CISM formulation are to be combined and catalytically sequenced in such a manner so as to yield the most efficient and effective crisis intervention possible. The various combinations and permutations that are actually utilized within the CISM model will be determined by the specific needs of each critical incident or traumatic event, as they uniquely arise. The current integrated, multi-component nature of CISM was not commonly practiced, nor was it fully developed, in its formative years. Historically, excessive reliance was placed upon one specific small group crisis intervention component of the overall CISM formulation. An over-utilization of the Critical Incident Stress Debriefing (CISD) intervention seemed clearly in evidence due to its ease of utilization and apparent effectiveness. Such an over-utilization of CISD was not to be unexpected, therefore.

The Early Years

Originally, Mitchell (1983) used the term CISD as an overarching label to refer to a strategic multi-componential approach to crisis intervention that contained four elements: 1) individual or group *on-scene* crisis intervention, 2) an initial post-incident small group discussion referred to as a *defusing*, 3) a more formalized post-incident 6-phase (later expanded to 7 phases) small group discussion referred to as the *formal CISD*, and 4) follow-up psychological support services. As can be imagined, the author's use of the term CISD to denote both 1) the overarching strategic approach to crisis intervention, as well as 2) a "formal" small group discussion process led to significant confusion, which persists even today! Nevertheless, the ease and perceived effectiveness of CISD guaranteed its proliferation.

Natural Evolution

As a direct result of the confusion created by the dual usage of the term CISD, and more importantly the inferred, but erroneous, tacit endorsement of CISD (the small group discussion) as a singular stand-alone crisis intervention, the term CISD, as the label for the cumulative strategic crisis intervention system, was abandoned in favor of the term Critical Incident Stress Management (CISM; Everly & Mitchell, 1999).

So, we see the term CISD was originally used to denote an integrated response system, as well as a small group crisis intervention. The former denotation was subsequently abandoned in favor of the term CISM to denote an integrated crisis intervention system, albeit somewhat limited in scope. The CISM construction was one of the first intervention models adopted as the field of disaster mental health was born and grew in popularity. As the complex idiographic heterogeneity of varied crisis and disaster situations were better understood, so the scope and complexity of CISM responded to meet those needs. CISM now represents a wide array of intervention options. Let us now turn to a review of a number of the core elements of the integrated multi-component CISM formulation.

The integrated and comprehensive multi-component CISM system is depicted in Table 5.1.

Table 5.1
Multi-Component Elements of CISM

INTERVENTION	TIMING	TARGET GROUP	POTENTIAL GOALS
I. **Pre-event** **Planning/** **Preparation**	Pre-event	Anticipated target/ victim population	Anticipatory guidance, foster resistance, resilience.
II. **Surveillance** **& Assessment**	Pre-event & during event	Those directly & indirectly exposed	Determination of need for intervention.
III. **Strategic** **Planning**	Pre-event & during event	Anticipated exposed & victim populations	Improve overall crisis response.
IV. **Individual Crisis** **Intervention** including "psychological first aid" (PFA) & SAFER-R	As needed	Individuals as needed	Assessment, screening, education, normalization, reduction of acute distress, triage, and facilitation of continued support.
V. **Large Group Crisis** **Intervention**			
A. "RIT" - Rest, Information, & Transition (also known as *demobil-ization*)	Shift disengagement; end of deployment	Emergency personnel	Decompression, ease transition, screening, triage, education and meet basic needs.
B. Respite center	Ongoing, largescale events	Emergency personnel, large groups	Respite, refreshment, screening, triage and support.

C. Crisis Mgmt. Briefing (CMB) and large group "psychological first aid"	As needed	Heterogeneous large groups	Inform, control rumors, increase cohesion.
VI. **Small Group Crisis Intervention**			
A. Small Group Crisis Mgmt. Briefing (sCMB).	On-going & post-event; may be repeated as needed	Small groups seeking information and/or resources	Information, control rumors, reduce acute distress, increase cohesion, facilitate resilience, screening and triage.
B. ISGS - Immediate Small Group Support (also known as *defusing*) and small group "psychological first aid"	within 12 hrs post-events	Small homogeneous groups	Stabilization, ventilation, reduce acute distress, screening, information, increase cohesion, and facilitate resilience
C. PEGS - Powerful Event Group Support [also known as *Critical Incident Stress Debriefing* (*CISD*)].	Post-event: ~ 1-10 days for acute incidents; ~ 3-4 wks. post-disaster recovery phase	Small homogeneous groups with equal trauma exposure (e.g., workgroups, emergency serv., and military)	Increase cohesion, ventilation, information, normalization, reduce acute distress, facilitate resilience, screening and triage. Follow-up essential.
VII. **Family Crisis Intervention**	Pre-event; or post-event as needed	Families	Wide range of interventions (e.g., pre-event preparation, individual crisis intervention, sCMB,PEGS or other group processes.)
VIII. **Organizational/ Community Intervention**	As needed	Organizations/ communities affected by trauma or disaster response.	Improve organizational, community preparedness. Leadership consultation.
IX. **Pastoral Crisis Intervention**	As needed	Individuals, small groups, large groups, congregations, & communities who desire faith-based presence/crisis intervention	Faith-based support
X. **Follow-up and/or Referral; Facilitating access to continued care**	As needed	Intervention recipients and exposed individuals	Assure continuity of care

This list of components has been significantly modified from a tactical perspective and has been strategically expanded since originally introduced. The expansion of CISM has been a direct result of its utilization beyond its original role of serving emergency services personnel subsequent to well-circumscribed critical incidents and its more recent applications to disasters, military venues, and terrorist-related situations. It may be argued that such tactical modification and strategic expansion represents the avoidance of stagnation and is an imperative dynamic for a healthy system. The extant 10 core CISM elements are discussed in some detail on the following pages.

1. Pre-incident preparation and training (Kaminsky, McCabe, Langlieb, & Everly, 2005, 2007)

This component of the CISM system refers to the processes of psychological and behavioral preparation designed to assist individuals in adjusting to an anticipated critical incident or traumatic event, prior to its actual occurrence. The goals of pre-incident preparation are to set the appropriate expectancies for personnel as to the nature of the crisis and trauma risk factors they may face. The corollary of this expectancy is to teach basic crisis coping skills in a proactive manner.

Historically, this element of CISM was conspicuous in it absence. More specifically, crisis intervention services were almost exclusively reactionary in nature. This element represents a proactive step in emergency mental health. Notions of psychological immunization and "psychological body armor" are engendered by the introduction of this intervention to the pre-incident phase of the critical incident temporal continuum. Perhaps the most recent evolution in pre-incident preparation would be the addition of specialized training in the emerging field of "psychological counterterrorism" (Everly & Castellano, 2005). Such an initiative has already begun within the law enforcement profession.

2. Surveillance and Assessment

Surveillance and assessment refers to the active process wherein the actual need for intervention is assessed and is predicated upon a population-based mechanism that identifies those who might benefit from intervention . Assessment may be performed upon individuals, small groups, and even large groups. The assumption that exposure to a traumatic event is the necessary and sufficient condition for active mental health intervention is a weak, if not false, assumption. Intervention should be predicated upon a demonstrated behavioral need or a request for intervention. Surveillance is but the initial step in a continuum that leads to assessment and ultimately intervention.

As previously mentioned, historically, crisis and disaster intervention systems have neglected this essential element (see Mitchell, et al., 2007).

3. Strategic Planning (Everly & Mitchell, 1999; Mitchell, 2007)

Strategic planning is a relatively new concept in applied critical incident response. It is based upon effective surveillance and assessment. While always implicit, its expressed importance and functional guidelines have only recently been delineated in a detailed manner. As noted, CISM represents, both strategically and tactically, an integrated, multi-faceted approach to crisis intervention. Strategic planning is the embodiment of Millon's (Millon, Grossman, Meagher, Millon, & Everly, 1999) concepts of *potentiating pairings and catalytic sequences* [defined earlier in this chapter]. Specific crisis interventions within are to be combined and sequenced in such a manner so as to yield the most efficient and effective crisis intervention possible.

4. Individual crisis intervention.

Crisis intervention with individuals, one at a time, is an essential element in the CISM approach. This form of crisis intervention is the most widely used of all crisis interventions, whether it is face-to-face or via telephone, as in a telephone hotline. This form of crisis intervention remains the most widely used form of crisis intervention and disaster response mechanism.

Historically, individual (one-on-one) crisis intervention was practiced in a virtual vacuum without recognition of the wide array of additional intervention tactics that were available (such as those enumerated on this list). For example, while potentially effective, one-on-one crisis intervention, by definition and practice, lacks the added advantages ("curative factors") of any form of group crisis intervention (see Yalom, 1970), when such is indicated. One-on-one crisis intervention may be paired with each of the other interventions on this list consonant with Millon's notion of potentiating pairings. [See Chapter Ten for a detailed discussion of Individual Crisis Interventions.]

5. Large Group Crisis Interventions

a. Rest, Information, & Transition (RIT). Also known as a *demobilization*, RIT represents an event-driven approach to crisis intervention often used for public safety, rescue, and emergency services personnel subsequent to a large scale crisis or disaster. Developed by Mitchell (see Mitchell & Everly, 1993, 2001) to mitigate stress reactions in large groups of emergency response personnel who might be secondary victims of trauma, the RIT is a combination of physical nourishment and stress management education. An alternative term for the process was thought useful to sufficiently differentiate this intervention from the military use of the term *demobilization*.

b. Respite sectors. Respite centers provide on-going support to disaster workers 24 hours a day. The respite center provides meals, supplies, a rest area, and other services to disaster personnel.

c. **Crisis Management Briefing (CMB; Everly, 2000a).** A CMB represents a form of "town meeting," or assembly, designed to facilitate social support, mitigate the spread of dysfunctional rumors, and provide functional empowering information for large groups (possibly as many as 300 or more at a time). This event-driven intervention attempts to achieve these goals almost exclusively through the provision of information to those groups affected by the event. It appears to be well suited for business and industrial applications, schools (Newman, 2000), and large scale community critical incidents such as violence, terrorist activities, and even most other community adversity. The CMB may be used in military applications as well. The CMB consists of 4 phases:

Phase One – Assembly. In this initial phase of the CMB, crisis interventionists identify the target group(s) for the intervention. The logistics of how and when to bring these individuals together is addressed. In a school setting, for example, each grade may be brought together, one grade at a time, in the school auditorium for the purpose of conducting the CMB. In the case of a high school, four sequential CMBs could be conducted, one for each grade.

Phase Two – Facts. In this phase anxieties are reduced and rumors are controlled by a direct presentation concerning what is known and what is not known about the critical incident. Care is taken not to breach boundaries of confidentiality.

Phase Three - Reactions. In this phase the discussion turns to common psychological and behavioral reactions engendered by similar critical incidents. Major psychological themes are anticipated and discussed. An effort is made to normalize reactions, as appropriate.

Phase Four – Coping Strategies and Resources. This final phase of the CMB consists of providing the group with specific personal and community resources that may assist in the restoration and recovery process. Stress management techniques are often discussed. Final questions are answered. Each person leaves the CMB with a sheet of paper that discusses common reactions, common coping techniques, and a list of community resources that may be used to facilitate the recovery process.

The CMB can also be used to triage individuals for more intense and appropriate intervention. In some critical incidents, victims may receive 3 or 4 serial crisis interventions. For example, victims may receive the CMB, then those who require further attention may later receive CISD or PEGS, and finally individual (one-on-one) crisis intervention, if necessary.

Looking at these large group interventions from an historical perspective, the *demobilization* (also known as Rest, Information, & Transition - RIT) was an opportunity for temporary psychological "decompression" immediately after exposure to a critical incident, typically applied at the point of shift disengagement.

While rooted in military psychiatry (Salmon, 1919; Artiss, 1963), the concepts of providing physical rest, nutrition, and psychoeducation have been employed and expanded through the development of the *respite center*. Respite centers, as noted, have been utilized in response to sustained rescue and recovery operations in the wake of large scale disasters. The American Red Cross pioneered the extant model of an on-going respite center in their response to the World Trade Center terrorist attacks. Respite centers were established in large buildings, hotels, and even large boats.

The *crisis management briefing* (CMB) was historically referred to as a "group informational briefing" (Everly & Mitchell, 1999); the process was refined and later referred to as the CMB (Everly, 2000a). It appears to be suited not only for disasters but also for business and industrial applications, schools (Newman, 2000), and large scale community critical incidents such as violence, terrorist activities, and most other community adversity. The CMB may be used in military applications as well. This intervention may be done within hours of the crisis event and may be repeated as often as necessary. The CMB was employed by the New York City Police Department in the wake of September 11. A much larger and longer (a two day residential variation) CMB was employed by the Port Authority Police of New York and New Jersey, also subsequent to the terrorist attacks of September 11, 2001. In 2007, the convocation in the wake of the shootings at Virginia Polytechnic University was a "textbook" CMB. Homogeneous groups are not necessary.

6. Small Group Crisis Interventions

a. Small group crisis management briefing (sCMB) The
sCMB has reportedly been used in military settings for those functional units exposed to a highly stressful incident, but for whom interaction may be premature. The sCMB follows the same informational structure as the large group CMB; only the group size is different.

b. Defusings/Immediate Small Group Support (ISGS).
Historically, the ISGS was referred to and developed as *defusing* (Mitchell, 2007, 1983b; Mitchell & Everly, 2001). The term was changed to ISGS for use within United Nations CISMu initiatives. It is one variation on the theme of small homogeneous group (< 20 individuals) crisis intervention. The defusing process is usually applied as soon as reasonably possible following a traumatic event, typically within 12 hours.

It has three segments. The first is a brief **introduction** of the trained team members who are co-leading the short meeting. The second segment is a **brief discussion** or exploration of the event itself. This discussion is very broad in scope. It is not necessary to gain a detailed rendition of the event. All that is necessary is that the people involved in the event discuss some of the key elements of the experience. The discussion is guided by questions from the trained team members. The third segment of the defusing/ISGS is the **practical information** provided by the intervention team to the group.

The entire defusing/ISGS process usually lasts between 20 and 45 minutes, depending on the size of the small group and the intensity of the situation. Closure is not necessarily the primary goal of this process. Instead, defusing/ISGS serves as a screening opportunity and a possible starting point for entry into other support services. Individual follow-up contacts should be initiated by the team providing the ISGS as soon as possible after the conclusion of the meeting. Follow-up services, other support processes and referrals, if necessary, should be instituted according to the needs of individuals or the group.

c. Critical Incident Stress Debriefing (CISD)/Powerful Event Group Support (PEGS). The term Powerful Event Group Support (PEGS) defines and describes the small group crisis intervention process as utilized by the United Nations. As the name Powerful Event Group Support implies, the only time this intervention is used is in the aftermath of a **powerful** traumatic **event**. The word **group** indicates that the process is for small groups. Group process literature commonly describes a small group as a primary or homogeneous group. A primary or homogeneous group shares a common *history*; its members have spent *time* together; and there are usually established *relationships* between the group members (Mitchell, 2007). Finally, the word **support** indicates that it maintains or sustains a group.

No one should construe the CISD/PEGS process to be a therapy process. The expressed goals are acute mitigation of distress, psychological closure, if possible, and to serve as a platform for facilitating access to continued care, if necessary. Psychological closure, operationally, is generally thought to mean a facilitation of psychological and behavioral reconstruction, or rebuilding, in the wake of a crisis or trauma.

The CISD/PEGS process has seven segments.
1) Introduction of the team and the group process
2) Facts/Brief situation review
3) Thoughts/First impressions
4) Reactions/Aspects of the event that had the greatest personal impact
5) Symptoms/Signals of distress
6) Teaching/Information and recovery guidelines
7) Re-entry/Summary

[For a more in depth discussion and description of the ISGS and PEGS processes as well as a comparison of PEGS to CISD, please go to Chapter 13.]

7. Family crisis intervention.

Family crisis intervention refers to the provision of acute psychological support to the family units of emergency services personnel, military members, and even civilian employees subsequent to violence, disasters, and other critical incidents at work.

Historically, families were often left out of the crisis intervention response. The military has done the most to see that acute mental health services are made available to family members whether they be primary, secondary, or tertiary victims. "Spouses of disasters workers need to be educated about their loved one's experiences. Many workers claimed that they wished their spouses had been informed of the nature of their work. Information can be provided to spouses in order to allay their concerns. This will also reinforce this naturally occurring support system. Brief groups held for spouses can also be a useful intervention" (Ursano, McCarroll, & Fullerton, 2003, p. 328).

8. Pastoral crisis intervention.

Pastoral crisis intervention (Everly, 2000b, 2000c; Everly, 2007) refers to the utilization of specially trained faith-oriented personnel in the provision of acute psychological support during or anytime after a critical incident or mass disaster.

Historically, utilization of the faith-based community during and after critical incidents was often a "catch as catch can" process. Some of those called upon possessed extraordinary training and competence in crisis intervention, while the only qualification for others was ordination. The pastoral crisis intervention movement simply mandates that those from the faith-based community who function in the field of crisis intervention and disaster response receive specialized training in emergency/disaster mental health response to critical incidents and mass disasters.

9. Organizational consultation and development.

Emergency mental health consultation and organizational development with institutional management/command staff is another important aspect of CISM. Here, the role of emergency mental health becomes assistance in strategic planning and consultation on tactical situations from a psychological perspective.

Historically, such a consultation function was seldom existent. When indeed present, such consultation was subsumed within the overall "health" function within a given organization or community. Now emergency mental health may be seen as a unique expertise, making a valuable contribution in its own right. As a result, this function has evolved to become a potential constituent of the Emergency/ Disaster Operations Center within the overall Incident Command System (ICS). "Organizational interventions after disasters and terrorism may be very important for assisting the recovery of the community. Leaders often find consultation about the expected human responses, phases of recovery, timing of recovery, identification of high-risk groups, and the monitoring of rest, respite, and leadership stress to be helpful" (Ursano et al., 2003, p. 335).

10. Follow-up and referral.

One of the great values of CISM services is that they serve as a feeder system, or facilitator, for the utilization of employee assistance programs and other mental health assessment and treatment services. Without crisis support services such as these it is likely that many individuals who need such follow-up care would simply not obtain it. DeGaglia (2006) has shown that emergency personnel are more willing to seek further care after receiving crisis intervention services.

Thus, follow-up with individuals, groups, and even communities, subsequent to the initial crisis intervention, and the facilitation of access to the next level of formalized medical and/or psychological intervention becomes an absolutely essential aspect of CISM.

Historically, crisis intervention was often seen as a "one shot" intervention. Now, both strategically and tactically, emergency mental health should be viewed as one point on an integrated continuum of care (British Psychological Society, 1990; Everly & Mitchell, 1999; Professional Practice Working Group, 2002; Ursano et al., 2003). It is this aspect that ensures the applicability of CISM and other systems' approaches (such as the American Red Cross, NOVA, and the Salvation Army) to all victims of trauma and disaster, regardless of the severity of manifest distress. Often, successful crisis intervention is defined simply by identifying those victims who require more intense intervention than acute psychological support (Ursano et al., 2003). In emergency medicine a successful intervention may be defined by having the emergency medical technicians simply "stabilize and transport" the medical patient, rather than achieving a "cure." Successful intervention in the field of emergency mental health may be defined as having the crisis interventionist stabilize and facilitate access to the next level of care, rather than affecting a "cure." Thus, screening and triage may be considered as successful outcomes in both physical medicine as well as emergency mental health.

SUMMARY

In this chapter, we have examined Critical Incident Stress Management (CISM) as a strategic delivery platform for providing integrated and comprehensive multi-component psychological/ behavioral services in the wake of critical incidents large and small.

CISM represents, both strategically and tactically, an integrated, multi-faceted approach to crisis intervention and disaster response. Consistent with Theodore Millon's (Millon, Grossman, Meagher, Millon, & Everly, 1999) integrative concepts, the *polythetic nature* of the CISM approach (selecting the tactical interventions as determined by the specific needs of each crisis situation), specific crisis interventions within the CISM formulation are to be combined and sequenced in such a manner so as to yield the most efficient and effective crisis intervention possible. The various combinations and permutations that are actually utilized within the CISM model will be determined by the specific needs of each critical incident or traumatic event, as they uniquely arise. The current integrated, multi-component nature of CISM was not commonly practiced, nor was it fully developed in its formative years, but has been seen to evolve with the recognized demands of the field.

CHAPTER SIX

Mechanisms of Action

"In light of research suggesting that crisis intervention can exert positive effects, efforts should be directed toward identifying mechanisms of therapeutic effect, potential sources of adverse iatrogenesis, and compensatory strategies developed to respond to the latter" (Everly, 2003, p. 180).

The term **mechanisms of action** refers to the mechanisms, or processes, through which any given intervention exerts its effect.

The notion of mechanisms of action, in essence, then refers to the processes that cause the intervention to be effective. In the study of psychopharmacology, for example, an understanding of the mechanisms of psychoactive drugs is considered essential to the viability and utilization of the drug. Drugs are sometimes prescribed for their "side effects" as well as their "main effects." But in general, the use of any drug is made more effective by understanding not just if it works, but how it works. The drug class known as selective serotonergic reuptake inhibitors, for example, derive its effectiveness from the ability to block the natural reuptake of the neurotransmitter serotonin at the presynaptic membranes. With this insight into the mechanisms behind the effectiveness of the medication, it may be utilized more effectively and perhaps applied in situations not originally considered. The mechanisms of action for psychological and behavioral interventions are usually more subtle and less well understood. Nevertheless, any intervention that exerts any effect at all must, by definition, have some mechanism of action that accounts for that effect. Psychological interventions most likely have many complex interacting mechanisms at the root of their effectiveness. While more complicated in terms of processes, the necessity to understand the mechanisms of action undergirding psychological and behavioral interventions is no less important.

The study of putative mechanisms of action is an important one if we are to improve our interventions and continue to innovate. Such scrutiny teaches us why our interventions succeed and why they fail; they allow us to "troubleshoot" complicated situations, as well.

The previous chapters provided a working overview of the interventions that comprise integrated, multi-component intervention systems in general, and the Critical Incident Stress Management (CISM) crisis response system specifically. The next logical step in understanding the integrative systems approach to intervention is an analysis of the mechanisms by which such integrative systems exert their effects.

PRINCIPLES OF CRISIS INTERVENTION AND DISASTER MENTAL HEALTH

As we reviewed in Chapter One the practice of the art of crisis intervention is very different than the practice of the art of psychotherapy. While both are obviously based upon basic communication skills and one's ability to relate in a meaningful way to others, they are indeed different and require different training formulations and experiences.

Salmon (1919), and Artiss (1963), as well as Kardiner and Spiegel (1947), writing about the lessons learned in emergency psychiatry during the world wars, noted that the emergency provision of care during a psychological crisis is different than traditional psychotherapy applications. From their analyses emerged three important principles of the crisis intervention process, PIE:

- Proximity - close to or within the physical venue of the crisis event, outreach
- Immediacy - rapid intervention, urgency
- Expectancy - setting appropriate expectations for the cause of the crisis and for intervention outcome

In a later analysis of crisis intervention within the context of a psychiatric emergency, Slaby and his co-workers (Slaby, Lieb, & Tancredi, 1975) pointed to the key factors in successful intervention as

- Immediacy (i.e., rapid intervention),
- Innovation (i.e., creative and flexible intervention), and
- Pragmatism (i.e., practical, goal-directed, action-oriented intervention. Some might think of this as "common sense").

In a more recent review of psychiatric therapies, Spiegel and Classen (1995) analyzed the processes that undergird crisis intervention. They are as follows:

- Immediacy in timing of the intervention,
- Social support, listening,
- Ventilation of emotion (catharsis),
- Commonality of experience as shared by those who participated in the same or similar crisis,
- Cognitive processing of the crisis,
- Anticipatory guidance (i.e., anticipating for the person in distress), and
- Educating, normalizing, and teaching coping responses.

CURATIVE FACTORS IN GROUPS

In the 1960s and 1970s group dynamics and group therapy were popular phenomena of inquiry. One of the most knowledgeable of writers and practitioners was Irving Yalom. Yalom (1970) wrote a classic textbook on group therapy. In his text, Yalom reported on a survey that he had conducted in which he asked participants in group therapy what the "curative" factors were that facilitated improvement. The factors perceived as most important by Yalom's respondents are as follows, listed in descending order of importance:

- Interpersonal learning (i.e. learning from other group members,
- Catharsis (i.e., the ventilation of emotions),
- Cohesiveness (i.e., relating to and with others in such a manner as to feel an integral part of the group and to identify with the group),
- Personal insight (i.e., knowledge gained about oneself through introspection and information from others),
- Interpersonal teaching of others,
- Existential awareness,
- Universality (i.e., destruction of the myth of unique vulnerability or unique weakness), and
- Instillation of hope.

All of these factors are potentially active in not just therapy groups, but crisis intervention groups as well.

FACTORS IN CRISIS INTERVENTION GROUPS

Recognizing the popularity and widespread utilization of crisis intervention groups, Wollman (1993) analyzed the bases for their effectiveness. His findings are as follows:

- Group cohesion,
- Universality,
- Catharsis,
- Imitative behavior,
- Instillation of hope,

- Imparting of information (teaching),
- Altruism,
- Timeliness, and
- Existential factors.

A review of these factors reveals that in Wollman's opinion, crisis intervention groups are effective for many of the same reasons that psychotherapy groups are effective, but with the added advantage of timeliness (i.e., "immediacy" in the language of crisis intervention).

MECHANISMS ACTIVE IN INTEGRATIVE SYSTEMS

It was the famous Johns Hopkins physician, Sir William Osler, who said, "To study the phenomenology of medicine without reading . . . is like sailing an uncharted sea."

Having reviewed the specific interventions and the previous literatures, we are in a much better position to speculate upon the mechanisms of action inherent in the comprehensive integrative approach to crisis and disaster response.

As noted earlier, behavioral and psychological interventions are not likely to derive their effectiveness from a single monolithic action (referred to as a main effect in analysis of variance parlance). Rather, behavioral and psychological interventions are far more likely to derive their effectiveness from interacting factors, or variables. Thus, they represent interaction effects. As the effects of interacting variables seldom are additive, but are synergistically multiplicative, even rigorous components analyses are seldom capable of ascribing relative weights to interacting variables in a manner that is valid for all individuals. So rather than estimate their relative values, we have simply chosen to offer the following four factors as those which we believe are the core process "mechanisms of action." They are the following.

101

Early Intervention

CISM interventions are designed to be implemented during the acute crisis phase (i.e., in the form of in-the-field on-scene support) and as quickly after the acute crisis event as possible. There is simply nothing quicker by design. Early, if not immediate, intervention has long been recognized as an important aspect of crisis response.

Salmon (1919) and Artiss (1963) noted the importance of rapid, emergency-oriented psychiatric intervention in World War I and World War II, respectively.

Lindy's (1985) notion of the trauma membrane argues that after a traumatic event victims begin to "insulate" themselves from the world through the construction of a "trauma membrane," or protective shell. The longer one waits to penetrate the shell, the more difficult it becomes, according to this formulation.

Earlier, Rapoport (1965) argued for the practical importance of early intervention, as did Spiegel and Classen (1995) in their review of emergency psychiatry.

Empirically, Bordow and Porritt (1979) were probably the first to test the importance of early crisis response. Their results support the conclusion that immediate intervention is more effective than delayed intervention.

Campfield and Hills (2000), in a randomized trial, showed that intervention applied early was superior to intervention applied later.

Solomon and Benbenishty (1986) empirically analyzed the three tenets of crisis response: immediacy, proximity, and expectancy. Each of the three was found to exert a positive effect. Their 20 year follow-up investigation (Solomon, Shklar, & Mikulincer, 2005) provided further validity to the importance of early intervention, showing that the elements of PIE exerted long-term protective effects.

Lastly, Post (1992), in a most provocative paper, argues that early intervention may prevent a genetically-based lowered threshold for neurological excitation from developing in response to trauma. Thus, early intervention may prevent the development of a cellular "memory" of trauma from being transmitted to excitatory neural tissues.

The Provision of Psychosocial Support

All human beings require some form of support from others (i.e., psychosocial support). Such support may come in the form of esteem, friendship, respect, trust, aid in problem-solving, or merely listening. Crisis accentuates this need.

American psychologist Carl Rogers wrote cogently in his theory of self psychology that all humans have an innate need for "positive regard" (Rogers, 1951). They possess a need to be valued by others.

Bowlby (1969) argues that there exists a biological drive for the bonding, or attachment, between humans, especially between mother and child.

Similarly, Maslow (1970) has written most coherently that one of the basic human needs is the need for social affiliation with others. According to Maslovian theory, many crises result from a loss of social support/affiliation.

Jerome Frank (1974), in his analysis of psychotherapy, argues that all psychotherapeutic improvement is based on the intervention's ability to reduce demoralization, especially through contradicting the notion of alienation. Individuals in crisis often feel alone, uniquely plagued, and abandoned.

By its very existence, any form of crisis response initiates the process of social support. It contradicts the alienation phenomenon, shows caring, and shows that the person in crisis is valued by others. It also contradicts any sense of abandonment.

The empirical evidence for social support as an effective crisis response tactic is persuasive. Buckley, Blanchard, and Hickling (1996) found an inverse relationship between social support and the prevalence of posttraumatic stress disorder in the wake of motor vehicle accidents. Bunn and Clarke (1979), in an early study of crisis intervention technologies, found that as crisis counseling services were provided, in the form of 20 minutes of supportive counseling, anxiety levels diminished. Dalgleish and colleagues (1996) also confirmed the assumption that social support is inversely correlated with posttraumatic stress-related symptoms.

Finally, Flannery (1990), in a comprehensive review of the role of social support in psychological trauma, found a general trend indicative of the value of social support in reducing the adverse impact of trauma.

The Opportunity for Expression

Bruno Bettleheim, an early psychotraumatologist, noted, "What cannot be talked about can also not be put to rest" (Bettleheim, 1984, p. 166). Much earlier, according to van der Hart and his co-workers (van der Hart, Brown, & van der Kolk, 1989) Pierre Janet declared in the late 1800s that successful recovery from trauma required the patient to verbally reconstruct and express the traumatic event.

The notion that recovery from trauma is predicated upon the verbal expression of not only emotions, but also cognitions, is virtually universal throughout crisis response literature. Spiegel and Classen (1995), in their review of crisis psychiatry, note the importance of cognitively processing the crisis.

Pennebaker and his colleagues, in an elegant series of empirical investigations, demonstrated the value of expression (Pennebaker, 1985, 1990, 1999; Pennebaker and Beall, 1986). Their investigations demonstrate the value of expression on not only psychological outcome measures but also physiological measures and behavioral measures.

In a random controlled trial, Koenig, Lating, and Kirkhart (2007) assessed the effects of allowing emotion-laden expression compared to a more cognitive (facts only) expression of a stressful/traumatic event. The authors state, "The results...are the first to provide evidence that talking about the emotions and facts of a highly stressful event leads to a decrease in pysiological arousal, whereas disclosing only the facts...does not" (p.181).

The notion of the value of cathartic ventilation has been challenged to the degree that concern has been expressed that cathartic ventilation may become a pathogenic abreactive process. While research has clearly demonstrated the value of expressing the factual nature of stressful events *in combination* with their associated emotions (Koenig, Lating, & Kirkhart, 2007; Pennebaker & Beall, 1986; Pennebaker, 1999), it is nevertheless conceivable that negative affect alone could crescendo inappropriately. To reduce this risk, it might be suggested that assessment and triage are essential elements of effective disaster mental health intervention wherein psychologically vulnerable or brittle persons (highly aroused, morbidly depressed, highly guilt-ridden individuals, the intensely bereaved, dissociating individuals, those experiencing psychotic symptomatology, those physically injured or in pain) not be included in group interventions; rather, they should be approached individually and more appropriate interventions should be utilized. Furthermore, whether individually or in groups, deep probing techniques, psychotherapeutic interpretation, and paradoxical intention should clearly be avoided.

Cognitive Interventions: Reframing, Explanatory Education, Anticipatory Guidance, and Coping

The fourth mechanism of action we find operating integrative systems involves the cognitive domain, more specifically

- cognitive reframing, wherein individuals are helped to see the incident or their reactions in a more constructive manner;
- explanatory education, referring to the provision of information that helps explain the nature of the incidents and/ or the nature of one's reaction;

- anticipatory guidance, referring to the provision of information that helps set appropriate expectations for reactions, intervention, and recovery; and
- stress management techniques that can be taught as a means of facilitating the coping process.

Persons in crisis commonly experience a sense of being out of control. Recovery (i.e., the restoration of psychological homeostasis and restoration of adaptive functioning) is often dependent upon reestablishing a sense of control. The perception of control is enhanced through setting appropriate expectations, developing a sense of understanding (Taylor, 1983), and teaching effective instrumental coping behaviors (Everly, 1989; Bandura, 1997).

Investigations and formulations by Taylor (1983) and Bandura (1997) argue convincingly for the power of mastery and perceived control as a mitigator of crisis, stress, and psychological discord. In his review of control and stress, Everly (1989) concludes that understanding, as induced by information/education, is a powerful stress reduction strategy. Further, Spiegel and Classen (1995) point out that cognitive processing of the crisis is also an important step toward resolution.

Thus, the operational corollaries of these formulations would be the following.

- Warn people in high risk environments as to the nature of their risk exposure and how to cope with crisis situations if they do occur (Hytten & Hasle, 1989; Weisaeth, 1989; Jonsson, 1995), as is done in pre-crisis preparation protocols (Mitchell & Everly, 1996).
- Sir Francis Bacon said information is power. Information and cognitive processing may lead to more rapid assimilation and a sense of mastery (Taylor, 1983; Pennebaker, 1999). Thus, provide needed information for better understanding of the nature of crisis and reactions to it.

- Teach practical techniques for reducing crisis exposure, mitigating the acute crisis response, facilitating reestablishment of homeostasis, and increasing the sense of self-efficacy (Bandura, 1997; Everly, 1989).

It has been proposed that health education regarding the signs and symptoms of distress may actually psychogenically create such symptoms in highly suggestible persons. It is hard to accept this notion of potential mass hysteria so as to "keep information from people for their own good." Nevertheless, it may be argued that the manner in which the information is presented may have a significant effect upon subsequent hysterical symptomatology. Such information should be presented as basic health education-related information and anticipatory guidance designed to empower the recipients of such information to assume more, not less, control in responding to adversity, when such seems appropriate.

SUMMARY

In this chapter, we have reviewed the concepts and mechanisms that are thought to serve as a foundation for integrative crisis and disaster response systems. In the final analysis we have concluded that four fundamental elements, or processes, are present:

- Early intervention,
- The provision of psychosocial support,
- The opportunity for expression, and
- Cognitive mechanisms.

CHAPTER SEVEN

Research on Crisis Intervention and Disaster Mental Health: Toward Evidence-based Practice

In this chapter, we shall review the research findings most relevant to the practice of integrative psychological crisis intervention and disaster mental health. In doing so, we acknowledge there is great difficulty in designing and implementing rigorous research in this field (NIMH, 2002; Bisson, Brayne, Ochberg, & Everly, 2007; Tuckey, 2007; Robinson, 2007). We further acknowledge that more research is needed. But that is not to say that there exists a vacuum of evidence in support of extant practices, nor is it to say that the existing evidence is inherently flawed and should be ignored. Let us take a closer look.

ISSUES OF DESIGN

Historically, behavioral science knowledge was based upon data generated from well-controlled efficacy research. Efficacy research typically used randomized experimental designs with one or more control groups contrasted against an experimental group to address issues of internal validation (Does the research answer the questions it purports to answer?). Further, ideally, subjects were chosen in such a manner so as to be a valid representative sample of a larger population to which the results of the research were to be generalized (external validity). Let us take a closer look at these forms of validity.

Internal Validity

The randomized controlled trial (RCT) is one wherein subjects are allocated to the experimental versus the control conditions on the basis of chance, using some randomization mechanism; thus in theory each subject has an equal likelihood of being assigned to the experimental or the control groups. The reason for using randomized subject assignment is to achieve groups that are equally weighted with regard to factors that might serve as alternative sources of effect. By equally distributing factors that may affect the measured outcome of the study to all of the groups in the research, the researcher hopes to isolate the treatment (independent variable) as the primary source of measured effect or outcome (dependent variable).

It is important to note, and a fact often overlooked by introductory textbooks, that *randomization is a process, not an outcome.* That is to say that even though the researcher may use random assignment of subjects, there is no assurance that equal groups actually will be created (Tuckey, 2007; Campbell & Stanley, 1963). In situations wherein randomization is used but equality of groups is not achieved, the investigation is likely to have sustained a fatal error that renders interpretation of the data impossible (Campbell & Stanley, 1963). That is, if the groups are unequal prior to the treatment, there is no way to be assured that differences after treatment are a result of the treatment, or are not caused by some other factor. Analysis of covariation may be attempted, but provides no absolute assurance as to causation.

So, for example, a researcher may wish to measure the effectiveness of a new medication. Patients are randomly assigned to the experimental group (those getting the new drug) and the control group (those getting sugar pills). Even though randomization (chance assignment) is used, it may turn out that those patients assigned to the experimental group are actually far more ill than those assigned to the control condition. If there is no difference in the groups at the end of the experiment, it may be falsely concluded that the new drug is no more effective than sugar.

In reality, there may have been improvement in the new drug group, but not enough to even out or surpass the pre-treatment differences. If pre-treatment measures are not taken into consideration, it may even be falsely concluded that the new drug made patients worse. The reader should keep this confounding issue in mind when we address the "debriefing debate" in the next chapter.

External Validity

The term **external validity** refers to the generalizability of the research data. Tebes (2000) has noted "…my colleagues and I, in our analysis of validity threats to experiments in real-world settings, have argued that, under some conditions, emphasizing internal validity over external validity in randomized trials may result in making incorrect causal inferences…If scientific psychology is to serve the public interest, its findings must be valid and generalizable and must promote the translation of research into informed public policy" (pp. 1508-1509).

A common mistake that researchers make is to over-generalize, i.e., to reach conclusions that are not supported beyond their subject pool. The researcher must ask if the subjects are a viable and representative sample of some larger population to which the results are to be generalized. For example, it is inappropriate to use a subject pool made up exclusively of males and then to generalize the results of the research to females if the researcher has any reason whatsoever to believe that sex differences themselves could influence that outcome of the study. Once again, the reader should keep this confounding issue in mind when we address the "debriefing debate" in the next chapter.

Beyond Efficacy Designs

Research designs which used nonrandomized assignment to experimental and control groups, as well as survey research, were once viewed as being of minimal value to the conduct of inquiry. These issues have traditionally plagued the field of psychotherapy research and, of course, the field of crisis response.

Pioneering psychologist and past president of the American Psychological Association, Dr. Martin Seligman (Seligman, 1995) has argued cogently for the power of nonrandomized experimental and even survey research designs. He notes, "I no longer believe that efficacy studies are the only, or even the best, way of finding out what treatments actually work in the field. I have come to believe that the 'effectiveness' study of how patients fare under the actual conditions ...in the field, can yield...'empirical validation' " (Seligman, 1995, p. 966). Seligman (1995) goes on to conclude, "Random assignment... may turn out to be worse than useless for the investigation of the actual treatment...in the field" (p. 974). He reaches this conclusion based upon the belief that efficacy studies are simply the wrong method for such research because they omit too many of the crucial elements that characterize what is actually done in the field, such as the level of competence of the interventionist, the real-time self-correcting nature of the intervention, and the complex nature of precipitating stressors. Similarly, it is important to keep in mind that randomized designs do not eliminate selection or assignment error; they simply serve to diminish the likelihood of systematic error. On the other hand, the effects of randomization may be approximated through the measurement of potential sources of systematic error, the use of large sample sizes drawn from diverse constituencies, and even meta-analytic approaches.

As we review research, the reader will see a wide variety of designs ranging from survey research and quasi-experimental, to forms of randomized assignment research and even meta-analysis.

INITIAL AND UNIVARIATE RESEARCH FINDINGS

It will be recalled that the evidence basis for crisis intervention and disaster mental health comes initially from the military psychiatry and the great world wars. Later, these principles were applied to civilian crisis situations and, later yet, to large-scale disasters.

Pioneer Dr. Thomas Salmon (1919) observed the use of the intervention principles of immediacy (urgency) and proximity ("treatment within the sound of artillery") utilized in the French *Postes de chirurgie d'urgence,* during World War I, where he observed 60% of cases of psychoneurosis were returned to combat after 7 days of treatment. He concluded, "Nothing could be more striking than the comparison between the cases treated near the front and those treated far behind the lines…As soon as treatment near the front became possible, symptoms disappeared…with the result that sixty percent with a diagnosis of psychoneurosis were returned to duty from the field hospital" (p. 994). Salmon's conclusions were based upon case study empiricism, but nevertheless shaped this aspect of military medicine for more than 80 years and continue to do so.

Kardiner (1959) observed the application of the crisis intervention principles of immediacy, proximity, and expectancy and noted, "Those on field duty found it to be most advantageous to the soldier, and to the army, to recognize exhaustion and the fear but not to remove the soldier to the rear" (p. 248). "By and large, the prognosis…varies directly with the time factor…The great issue…is not to permit the syndrome to become entrenched…" (p253). "The most effective implement is to keep alive the [causal] relation between the symptoms and the traumatic event" (as opposed to attributing symptoms to weakness in character; p. 254). In addition, Kardiner noted, to a significant degree, the soldier's expectation of outcome predicts recovery from war neurosis.

British psychiatrist William Sargant (1942) noted, "Our most important finding has been the supreme need for immediate first aid treatment of the acute neurosis…" (p 574).

Artiss (1963) concurred and commented on war neurosis, "Removal of the soldier from the front returned only five percent of such casualties to duty" (p. 1011). The treatment principles of immediacy, proximity, and expectancy were later applied and resulted in 70-80% of combat psychiatric casualties returning to duty.

The conclusions reached by Salmon, Kardiner, Sargant, and Artiss were based upon case study empiricism. This form of evidence must be considered weak, however, because of the myriad of alternative sources of effect.

Moving from naturalistic observations to designed manipulations, Shalev and colleagues (1998), based on the work of S.L.A. Marshall, administered the Historical Event Group Debriefing to 39 military personnel within 72 hours of a critical incident. A decrease in anxiety combined with an increase in self-efficacy and an increase in group cohesion was noted.

Deahl and colleagues (1994) tested the "Dyregrov model" of group psychological debriefing (PD) with military personnel ($n = $ 40 PD vs. 20 control). The PD was implemented as soon as possible, but was highly variable in actuality. No difference was discovered between groups at nine months. Dyregrov later noted that there was no such thing as a "Dyregrov model" of debriefing. He used Mitchell's CISD model.

Deahl et al. (2000), in a randomized controlled design, found small group crisis intervention (CISD) to be effective in reducing alcohol use in British military personnel returning from peace-keeping activities in a war zone. In a study of British UN peacekeeping troops returning from service in Bosnia, 106 soldiers received an operational stress training package before deployment, while half (randomly assigned) received psychological debriefing (CISD) upon their return. Although debriefing had no effect on rates of PTSD (a floor effect existed), it did reduce high rates of alcohol misuse in returning soldiers. More than 25% showed evidence of significant alcohol misuse immediately following their return. One year later only 16% were misusing alcohol, the reduction occurring almost exclusively in the debriefed group.

More recently, Hoge, Castro, Adler, McGurk, et al. (2006) conducted a randomized assessment of the efficacy of post-deployment psychological debriefing (CISD) with American soldiers. Within 3 days of return from deployment to a combat zone, 447 soldiers were randomly assigned to a CISD group intervention or a stress education group. Surveys conducted 4 months later revealed that for those with high levels of combat exposure, CISD was associated with lower post-trauma stress, depression, and anger scores, as well as higher life satisfaction scores.

In the formative years of crisis intervention as applied to the civilian world, Rapoport (1965) noted, "A little help, rationally directed and purposely focused at a strategic time, is more effective than extensive help given at a period of less emotional accessibility" (p. 30). Well controlled research would seem to support such a conclusion.

Langsley, Machotka, and Flomenhaft (1971) used random assignment (RCT) of 300 patients to inpatient treatment vs. family crisis intervention. Results indicated crisis intervention was superior to inpatient treatment for preventing subsequent psychiatric hospitalizations. Decker and Stubblebine (1972) followed 540 psychiatric patients for 2½ years subsequent to an initial psychiatric hospitalization. Traditional follow-up treatment was compared to crisis intervention services. Results supported the superiority of the crisis intervention services in preventing subsequent hospitalizations.

Bunn and Clarke (1979), in a randomized controlled design with 30 individuals who had accompanied relatives to the hospital after a serious injury, found 20 minutes of supportive crisis "counseling" superior to no intervention in reducing anxiety.

Stapleton and colleagues (2006) conducted a review and meta-analysis of 11 studies (10 randomized controlled trials) of crisis intervention with medical and surgical patients. The analysis included 2124 subjects. Stapleton and colleagues (2006) found crisis intervention to be generally effective overall (Cohen's $d = .44$), with specific mitigating effects on anxiety (.52), depression (.24), and posttraumatic stress (.57). Other findings of note were the following.

- Early psychological intervention is improved by increased interventionist training (Cohen's $d = .57$ vs. .29).

- Early psychological intervention outcome is enhanced via multiple sessions (Cohen's d = .60 vs .33).
- Early psychological intervention is enhanced via the use of multiple types of interventions (Cohen's d = .62 vs .55).

Robyn Robinson pioneered the use of group crisis intervention with emergency services personnel in Australia. She employed Mitchell's CISD protocol. Robyn Robinson and Jeffrey Mitchell (1993) used a survey designed to assess the effectiveness of one of the CISM interventions, CISD. Participants in the study consisted of 288 Australian emergency services, welfare, and hospital personnel who had taken part in 31 CISDs from December 1987 through August 1989. Responses were received from 172 (60%) of the surveyed group. Ninety-six percent of the emergency services personnel and 77% of the welfare and hospital personnel reported a reduction in crisis-related symptoms due, in part, to CISD.

In an investigation of the CISD intervention, specifically, Nancy Bohl (1991) assessed the mandatory CISD upon law enforcement officers who had experienced a critical incident. The effectiveness of the CISD was assessed 3 months post-incident, utilizing standardized written psychometrics. Officers who had received the CISD within 24 hours of the incident ($n = 40$) were compared to officers who received no CISD ($n = 31$). Those who received the CISD were found to be less depressed, less angry, and to possess fewer stress-related symptoms. Bohl's description of the control and experimental groups argues against evidence of systematic error in subject assignment and for a naturalistic randomization process.

In a follow-up investigation Bohl (1995) studied the effectiveness of CISD upon 30 firefighters who received the CISD compared with 35 firefighters who did not receive the CISD at about 24 hours after a critical incident. Anxiety symptoms measured at 3 months post-CISD were found to be lower in the CISD group compared to the control group.

The Los Angeles County's Fire Department (LACoFD) CISM program was evaluated through the dissemination of 3000 research surveys (Hokanson, 1997). Of the 3000 disseminated, 2124 were completed for a 70.8% return rate. Of the 2124 respondents, more than 600 indicated that they had participated in a Critical Incident Stress Debriefing (CISD).

As noted by Hokanson (1997), two of the explicitly stated goals of the CISM program are

- to accelerate the recovery process after a traumatic event and
- to reduce the adverse impact of a traumatic event.

According to the author, the LACoFD data support the effectiveness of the CISM program in achieving both of these goals (Hokanson, 1997). More specifically:

1) The CISD process was shown to be effective in accelerating the recovery process in response to traumatic events. A significant reduction of trauma-related symptoms was experienced by 56.3% of respondents within 72 hours after the CISD, compared to 45.5% indicating reduction of symptoms without the CISD in response to a comparable traumatic event. Thus the 72-hour incremental recovery utility for CISD was 10.8% beyond the natural recovery process. Further, 74.1% of respondents experienced a significant reduction of trauma-related symptoms within one week after the CISD, compared to 65.5% indicating reduction of symptoms without the CISD in response to a comparable traumatic event. Thus, the one-week incremental recovery utility for CISD was 8.6%.

Such findings have implications for medical utilization, sick leave, and workers compensation claims and therefore may have relevance for all workplace-based psychological support programs, including employee assistance programs.

2) The CISD process was shown to be effective in facilitating the amelioration of trauma-related symptoms. Of the respondents, only 13.9% indicated they had persistent trauma-related symptoms more than 6 months post-trauma and post-CISD, compared to 16.5% indicating persistent symptoms in response to a comparable trauma wherein no CISD was performed. Thus, the incremental recovery utility was 2.6% for the CISD in this analysis.

Such findings have implications for workers' compensation disability claims and the incidence of early retirement and general turnover.

On October 16, 1991 a mass shooting in a crowded cafeteria in Killeen, Texas left 55 people wounded; 23 people would die of their wounds. Emergency medical personnel from two local fire/rescue departments responded to this mass fatality incident. The state of Texas provided voluntary CISDs for the rescue personnel within 24 hours after the shooting. A total of 36 respondents participated in this longitudinal assessment of the effectiveness of the CISD interventions (Jenkins, 1996). Recovery from the trauma appeared to be most strongly associated with participation in the CISD process. CISD was useful in reducing symptoms of depression and anxiety for those who participated in the CISD compared to those who did not. The authors make a special point in indicating that this study addresses many of the common methodological problems existing in the debriefing literature, as described by Bisson and Deahl (1994).

When crisis intervention principles and practices were applied to victims of bank robberies, the crisis interventions were found to be effective in reducing distress. Campfield and Hills (2001) used a randomized design wherein groups of bank robbery victims were randomly assigned to a CISD group intervention conducted within 10 hours of the event in contrast to a CISD group intervention conducted more than 48 hours post robbery. Posttraumatic distress was assessed at 2 weeks. Results indicated that those who received the CISD intervention within 10 hours experienced less distress than those who received the CISD intervention later than that. In another investigation, Richards (1999) compared the CISD group crisis intervention to the multi-component CISM program. While both were effective crisis intervention technologies, the CISM program proved superior, as was predicted, thus underscoring the importance of an integrated, multi-component approach to crisis intervention.

The CISD intervention has found application not only in well circumscribed critical incidents, but in large-scale disasters as well. The CISD protocol was used subsequent to Hurricane Iniki for 41 crisis response personnel on the island of Kauai. The research cohort was divided into two groups for pre-test and post-test comparisons (Chemtob et al., 1997). To provide a control group paradigm, a time-lagged design was employed wherein the pre-treatment assessment of the second group was concurrent with the post-treatment assessment of the first group. Repeated ANOVA indicated that psychometrically assessed posttraumatic stress (Impact of Events Scale) was reduced in both groups as a result of the CISD intervention.

After the Los Angeles riots in 1992, researchers studied the impact of stress reactions on emergency medical services personnel and the effectiveness of CISD. Using the Frederick Reaction Index the researchers compared groups of emergency medical services personnel who had received debriefings with those who had not received the service after the same or very similar experiences in the riots. Those workers who were given an opportunity to participate in a Critical Incident Stress Debriefing session scored significantly lower on the Frederick Reaction Index compared with those not offered this service (Wee, Mills, & Koehler, 1999).

Wee's design argues for the absence of systematic assignment error, thus supporting the notion of naturalistic randomization in assignment for those who utilized the CISD compared to those who did not.

In 1994, Scandinavia suffered its worst peacetime sea disaster in history with the sinking of the ferry Estonia. More than 900 people perished. Nurmi (1999) contrasted three groups of emergency response personnel who received the CISD intervention with a group of emergency nurses who received support from their supervisors, but no CISD. Nurmi contrasted 38 frontier guards, 30 firefighters, and 26 disaster victim identification team members to 28 emergency room nurses. Data indicated that psychometrically assessed (Impact of Events Scale) symptoms of posttraumatic stress disorder several days post-incident were lower in each of the three groups that received the CISD. Nurmi notes that this was the largest application of the CISD model in Finnish history.

Carlier and colleagues (1998) conducted a study with law enforcement personnel. One group ($n = 46$) which received a CISD was compared to a control condition ($n = 59$). No difference was found at 8 months on a measure of PTSD. However, increased arousal was evident in the CISD group at 18 months in this non-randomized investigation.

Eid, Johnsen, and Weisaeth (2001) assessed the effectiveness of group CISD on 9 military personnel vs. 9 firefighters in a control condition following a fatal auto accident. Posttraumatic stress scores were seen to decline in the CISD group at 2 weeks.

Everly and Boyle (1999) performed a meta-analysis on the CISD model of psychological debriefing in an attempt to resolve equivocal data that had appeared in the current literature. Five peer reviewed studies were employed, including 341 subjects. Various self- report psychological measures were utilized; a positive effect ($d > .8$) for CISD group debriefings was found. The authors concluded that data suggests group psychological debriefing exerted an ameliorative effect upon symptoms of stress and trauma in the wake of vicarious exposure.

De Gaglia (2006) reported on data collected on three cohorts of full-time fire/rescue professionals: trauma-exposed participants who requested a small group crisis intervention (255), non-trauma-exposed participants (147), and trauma-exposed participants who received no intervention and were assessed 3 days after a trauma (34). The small group intervention was associated with lowered composite negative affect score (MAAC-R) whether compared to the pre-intervention score or the trauma-exposed group 3 days distant from the trauma who had received no intervention. Perhaps of greater importance was the finding that post-intervention, fire/rescue professionals agreed they were more likely to seek out future mental health services (2½ times) and future small group interventions (2 times).

MULTI-FACTORIAL PROGRAMS

Multi-factorial crisis response programs represent interventions that are representative of, or are in varying degrees of agreement with, the integrative formulations endorsed in this volume.

Somewhat prior to the current authors' formulations of CISM, the notion of an integrated, multi-factorial crisis intervention program was assessed in Australia. Bordow and Porritt (1979) employed a 3-group design contrasting 1) no intervention to 2) a one session "review" of facts and emotions, to 3) a multi-factorial intervention for victims of traffic traumas. The results of this random assignment investigation indicated that a one session crisis intervention was effective in the reduction of adverse effects of trauma, but further analysis revealed that the integrated, multi-factorial intervention was even more effective. Results were indicative of a dose response relationship between intervention level and the reduction of reported distress.

Brom, Kleber, and Hofman (1993) conducted an investigation of the primary victims of traffic trauma. A group of 151 subjects were randomly assigned to the intervention group and a control group. The intervention itself consisted of a multi-component program that combined "practical help," "information," "support," "reality testing," "confrontation with the experience," and "referral to psychotherapeutic treatment." While scores on the Impact of Events Scale failed to demonstrate differences between the monitoring control group and the experimental group, scores on the checklist of trauma symptoms did, indeed, show the effectiveness of the multi-factorial intervention.

Similarly, Busuttil and colleagues (1995) evaluated the Royal Air Forces' PTSD rehabilitation program (Wroughton). Their results indicated that a CISM-like intervention model was a useful technique for the reduction of the number of PTSD cases.

In a 1982 study of Israeli soldiers, Solomon and Benbenishty (1986) investigated the core crisis intervention principles of proximity, immediacy, and expectancy. Their investigation revealed that all three were positively correlated with returning to the fighting unit. Further analyses revealed that immediacy and expectancy were correlated inversely with the development of posttraumatic stress disorder. In support of the integrated, multi-factorial approach to crisis response, the authors conclude, "The effects of proximity, immediacy, and expectancy seem to be interrelated . . . the findings of this study clearly demonstrate the cumulative effect of implementing all three treatment principles" (Solomon & Benbenishty, 1986, p. 616). Most importantly, however, are the implications of the 20-year longitudinal follow-up by Solomon and colleagues (Solomon et al., 2005). Their study evaluated the long-term effectiveness of the frontline interventions provided to combat stress reaction casualties. Using a longitudinal quasi-experimental design, the same combat stress reaction casualties of the 1982 Lebanon War who received frontline treatment ($n = 79$) were compared to matched combat stress reaction casualties who did not receive frontline treatment ($n = 156$) and other soldiers who did not experience combat stress reaction ($n = 194$). Twenty years after the war, traumatized soldiers who received frontline crisis intervention, following the core principles of proximity, immediacy, expectancy, had lower rates of posttraumatic and psychiatric symptoms and reported better social functioning than similarly exposed soldiers who did not receive frontline intervention. The cumulative effect of the core crisis principles was documented in that the more principles applied, the stronger the effect. The authors conclude, "Frontline treatment is associated with improved outcomes even two decades after its application. This treatment may also be effective for nonmilitary precursors of posttraumatic stress disorder" (p. 2309).

The On Site Academy in Gardner, Massachusetts is a residential rehabilitation program for individuals who have experienced psychologically disabling symptoms from some form of traumatic experience. The On Site Academy's constituency is the emergency services personnel of North America. The Academy employs a short-term residential variation of the CISM program. A rationale for such utilization is that these individuals, so adversely affected by trauma, still find themselves in the midst of a psychological crisis, regardless of how much time has passed since the actual traumatization. The core components of the Academy's CISM program are the following.

- Training/education into the nature of stress, trauma, and crisis coping techniques
- CISD
- Paraprofessional peer support
- Individual counseling (at least 3 sessions)
- Eye Movement Desensitization and Reprocessing (EMDR)

In an evaluation of the On Site Academy's program, Manzi (1995) surveyed 108 participants, with a response of 45 returned surveys (41.7%). The average amount of time respondents had been out of the program was 10 months. Program participants were surveyed to inquire if the Academy's CISM program had met their expectations and goals; 100% indicated that it had. Further, 100% of the surveyed participants indicated they would recommend the Academy.

Further survey inquiry was made to assess the effectiveness of the Academy's CISM program in reducing trauma-related symptoms. Participants were asked to indicate, using symptom checklists, their symptomatic response to a traumatic event prior to entering the

Academy's program. They were then asked to indicate their current symptom response after completing the Academy's program. Symptoms were assessed, using this retrospective pre-test post-test design, in four domains: cognitive, emotional, behavioral, and physiologic. The investigation by Manzi (1995) revealed significant decreases in all four symptom domains from pre-CISM to post-CISM.

Following a successful pilot project on nursing stress (Kirwin, 1994) in the Manitoba region of Canada, the Medical Services Branch (MSB) authorized the implementation of a national CISM program for the Indian and Northern Health Services nurses. An integrated, multi-component CISM program was implemented. Subsequently these nurses were sampled to assess both the need for and the effectiveness of the CISM program.

Survey and interview data were collected, analyzed, and reviewed by an independent evaluation organization (Westen Management Consultants, 1996). Data were collected from nurses working in Pacific/British Columbia, Alberta, Manitoba, and Ontario. Of 582 nurses, 236 responded (41%).

As for need, the study revealed that 65% of the nurses experienced at least one critical incident per year in the workplace. These critical incidents included, but were not limited to

- Death of a child - 37% of nurses,
- Attempted or actual physical assault - 28%,
- Break-ins at nursing facilities - 25%,
- Verbal threats/assaults - 52%,
- Suicide or attempted suicide of a patient - 44%.

The CISM concept was operationalized and instituted as a means of reducing critical incident-related stress and discord. Some the results are summarized below.

- 82% of field nurses who had used CISM services reported that the services met or exceeded their expectations.

- 89% of field nurses indicated they were satisfied with the CISM services.
- 99% of the field nurses indicated that the CISM program reduced the number of days they were absent from work.

The evaluation report (Western Management Consultants, 1996) concluded, "Survey data suggest MSB CISM significantly reduced turnover among field nurses" (p. 53). As many as 24% of the nurses who experienced a critical incident contemplated leaving their jobs, but did not after a CISM intervention. It was estimated that it would cost CN$38,000 to replace a single nurse.

Further financial evaluations revealed a 7.09:1 financial benefit-to-cost ratio which may be seen as a greater than 700% return on investment. The authors of the evaluation report concluded, "It is evident that the quality of the existing program is exceptional. The MSB program is a state-of-the-art program that should be emulated by other employers, and sets a standard by which alternatives should be judged" (Western Management Consultants, 1996, p. iv).

The MSB CISM program is virtually a prototypic CISM program as prescribed by this volume.

Flannery (2001; Flannery, Hanson, & Penk, 1994; Flannery, Hanson, Penk, Flannery, & Gallagher, 1995) pioneered the development of a fully integrative, multi-component critical incident stress management program referred to as the Assaulted Staff Action Program (ASAP). Flannery's ASAP program is an exemplary CISM crisis intervention approach (Flannery, 1998) used in hospitals, clinics, and schools. Research has consistently shown the ASAP program to be an effective crisis intervention. In fact, the ASAP program was chosen as one of the 10 best programs in 1996 by the American Psychiatric Association.

For 15 years, Flannery's Assaulted Staff Action Program has been associated with providing psychological support to healthcare staff as well as contributing to declines in the frequency of assaults upon staff. The dependent variable in each of the five studies cited below is assaults (physical, sexual, verbal) by patients upon healthcare staff. The choice of assaults as a dependent variable may seem unusual in investigations of crisis intervention, but seems justified as an index of the overall psychological climate engendered as a result of rapid, multi-faceted crisis intervention. It is important to keep in mind the critical role that expectancy plays to affect positive outcome in the crisis intervention milieu (Solomon & Benbenishty, 1986). The ASAP intervention may derive its ability to generate the desired outcome via an alteration in the important crisis variable of expectancy, in addition to immediacy and proximity.

The original ASAP investigation was conducted in a 400-bed traditional state mental hospital with 415 direct care staff (Flannery, Hanson, Penk, Flannery, & Gallagher, 1995). In this single case design, the hospital base rate of 30 assaults per month prior to the ASAP CISM intervention declined to a rate of 11 per month after ASAP had been in place one year. Since the decline in frequency of assaults was reported in the first facility with ASAP, it raised the ethical issue of withholding an ASAP program from any facility that might serve as a traditional control. As a result, all further ASAP studies herein employed research designs wherein the facility served as its own control.

Flannery, Hanson, Penk, Goldfinger, Pastva, and Navon (1998) replicated the first ASAP study but used a multiple baseline design (Hersen & Barlow, 1976; Blampied, 2000). Three hospitals with size and staffing comparable to the original had their ASAP interventions come on-line at three-month staggered intervals. The combined base rate of 31 assaults per quarter prior to ASAP declined to 2.44 per quarter after ASAP had been in place for one year ($F = 80.85$; $df = 4,40$; $p < .001$).

The next replication occurred in a 16-bed community mental health center with 32 direct care staff (Flannery, Penk, & Corrigan, 1999).

The base rate for assaults prior to the ASAP CISM intervention was 11.25 per quarter. This declined to 0 after six quarters ($t = 12.93$; $df = 30$; $p < .001$).

The last two studies that sought to replicate the original finding of declines in assaults were conducted in a second community mental health center and in an intermediate care facility with combined totals of 125 beds and 159 direct care staff (Flannery, Anderson, Marks, & Uzoma, 2000). In the community mental health center, the base rate of assaults increased from 32 to 34 per year. In the intermediate care facility the base rate of 33 assaults per year declined to 25 per year after ASAP.

A 10-year review of ASAP practice revealed ASAP to be clinically effective (Flannery, 2001). In a follow-up investigation, Flannery, Rego, Farley, and Walker (in press) reported on the 15-year analysis of ASAP. The sample consisted of 1,071 male and 1,049 female inpatient and community mental health facility staff victims of patient assaults in the Massachusetts Department of Mental Health's seven inpatient state hospitals, five state community mental health centers, one state homeless shelter program, two vendor-operated sets of community residences, and one private general hospital that accepted DMH patients. The crisis intervention procedures were associated with sharp declines in disruptions in the three health domains and the three symptom clusters. The findings demonstrate significant recovery and functioning within a 10-day period associated with the CISM intervention.

Flannery and Everly (2004) conducted a descriptive review of CISM-related published research from 1998 through 2002. This was a follow-up to a previously conducted review that summarized CISM literature through 1997 (Everly, Flannery & Mitchell, 2000). The authors reviewed 20 papers and concluded that CISM approaches may represent one effective way to address the adverse psychological consequences associated with critical incidents.

In the wake of a terrorist mass casualty disaster, Boscarino et al., (2005) conducted a random sample of 1,681 New York adults interviewed by telephone at one year and two years after 9/11. Results indicate that crisis interventions, referred to as Critical Incident Stress Management (CISM), had a beneficial impact across a variety of outcomes, including reduced risks for binge drinking, alcohol dependence, PTSD symptoms, major depression, somatization, anxiety, and global impairment, compared with individuals who did not receive these interventions. In a follow-up analysis (Boscarino et al., 2006), found that 1-3 sessions of brief crisis intervention were useful at reducing various forms of distress from mass disasters.

Boscarino, Adams, Foa, and Landrigan (2006) utilized a propensity score analysis of brief worksite crisis interventions (referred to as CISM) after the World Trade Center disaster. In a prospective cohort design of 1121 subject employees, 150 received interventions. Interventions consisted of 1-3 brief interventions by a mental health clinician. Results indicated that the brief post-disaster interventions yielded positive outcome up to 2 years post-disaster in the forms of reduced depression, reduced alcohol dependence, reduced PTSD severity, and reduced anxiety.

Everly and colleagues (2006) employed a systematic statistical review of experimental and quasi-experimental research on workplace-based crisis intervention programs. Nine studies were identified that met inclusion criteria for further analysis. Results suggest that the workplace can be a useful platform from which to provide crisis intervention programs (overall effectiveness measured in the Cohen's d statistic expressed in standard deviations = 1.53; d = .60 with assaults removed from the analysis). More specifically, evidence was found that crisis intervention programs could reduce specific undesirable factors in the workplace.

- Posttraumatic distress: mean effect size = .65
- Assaults: mean effect size = 3.68

- Alcohol use: mean effect size = .83
- Depression = .81
- Anxiety = .98
- Global impairment: mean effect size = .166

SUMMARY

In this chapter, we have reviewed a wide array of studies that assess the effectiveness of univariate, multi-variate, and more comprehensive, integrated crisis and disaster mental health intervention programs.

Although methodological rigor is highly variable, given the wide variety of interventions across a wide dimension of subject populations, there would seem to be compelling evidence to support the continued use of and investigation of the CISD group crisis intervention as well as integrated crisis and disaster response programs.

Rather than blindly abandon or blindly endorse continued practice, there exist sufficient data herein to compel continued research in order to more clearly define active mechanisms of positive effect. Said another way, at this point in time, reaching a definitive conclusion regarding the overall effectiveness of crisis and disaster intervention programs seems misguided. More appropriate would be thoughtful analysis and continued investigations into which interventions work, with what populations, under what circumstances, and why; similarly, what does not work, and why not.

CHAPTER EIGHT

The "Debriefing Debate"

Despite a long and rich history as a specialty within applied mental health, as reviewed in the previous chapter, crisis intervention has, within recent years, been the target of criticism. Singled out for specific criticism has been the intervention referred to as "debriefing." Some authors have not only challenged its effectiveness, but have raised the specter that it may cause significant harm. While superficially such arguments appear to have merit, closer scrutiny reveals an antiquated interpretation of even the most fundamental of terms and concepts inextricably intertwined with research based upon applications contrary to the most recent principles, prescriptions, and protocols regarding clinical use. In this chapter, we will review the controversy surrounding "debriefing" with the goal of elucidating the most salient features. We shall see that the debate surrounding the utility of "debriefing" is complicated by confusion regarding terminology (the definition of **debriefing**), combined with the design of relevant research (what constitutes relevant research). As noted by Tuckey (2007), "Underlying the debriefing debate are conceptual confusions and methodological issues that have prevented experts from reaching agreement about the value of debriefing" (p. 106).

TERMINOLOGY

In previous chapters, we introduced the notion that there is some confusion over what a "debriefing" actually is. Let us review and take a closer look.

Kenardy (2000) has stated, "Psychological debriefing is broadly defined as a set of procedures including counseling and the giving of information aimed at preventing psychological morbidity and aiding recovery after a traumatic event" (p.1032). This definition of psychological debriefing, while anchored in the historical literature (Mitchell, 1983a), is clearly: a) not conducive to easily replicated empirical investigations due to a lack of specificity and standardization, and b) in opposition to more recent formulations which have evolved over the last 25 years wherein the term "debriefing" refers to a standardized group crisis intervention.

Historically, it will be recalled, Critical Incident Stress Debriefing (CISD) represents the oldest and most commonly used non-military form of psychological "debriefing" which employs a standardized structure. But the roots of group debriefing actually date back to the military applications during World War II. Nevertheless, CISD is the model from whence the currently used generic term "debriefing," in the psychological sense, was originally derived. Its originator, Jeffrey T. Mitchell, contends that CISD was never intended to be a "stand-alone" intervention nor a substitute for psychotherapy (Mitchell & Everly, 1997). Rather, the CISD is one form of group crisis intervention which represents but one component within a larger crisis and disaster intervention program referred to as Critical Incident Stress Management (Everly & Mitchell, 1999).

As a form of group crisis intervention, the CISD typically takes 1.5 to 3.0 hours to conduct. It is most commonly conducted 2 to 14 days after a critical incident. In cases of mass disasters, the CISD is not recommended until 3 to 4 weeks post disaster, or even later. The expressed intention of the CISD is to provide some facilitation of the process of psychological "closure" upon the traumatic, or critical, incident (i.e., the facilitation of the reconstruction process). When closure is not possible, the CISD may serve as a useful mechanism, or platform, for psychological triage so as to identify those who may need more advanced care.

As noted earlier, in Mitchell's seminal paper, Critical Incident Stress Debriefing (CISD) was described as follows, "The CISD is an organized approach to the management of stress responses in emergency services. It entails either an individual or group meeting…"(Mitchell, 1983, p. 37). He went on to describe a multi-component crisis intervention approach that included a small group crisis intervention, also referred to as a formal critical incident stress debriefing (CISD). Considerable semantic confusion resulted from Mitchell's use of the term CISD to denote more than one thing:

- the overarching framework for his crisis intervention system (CISD),
- a specific six-phase small group discussion process ("formal" CISD), and
- the optional follow-up intervention (follow-up CISD).

As a result, the current literature is plagued with references to "individual debriefings," and the perpetuated, but erroneous, notion that the CISD group discussion was intended to be a stand-alone, or "one-off" intervention. In an effort to rectify the lexical discord and expand the original formulations, the term Critical Incident Stress Management () was chosen as the term to denote the overarching, multi-component approach to crisis intervention, thus replacing the term CISD as it was originally used in that context. The term CISD is now used exclusively to denote what has become a specific seven-phase *group* crisis intervention process.

RESEARCH FINDINGS AND THE DEBRIEFING DEBATE

Initial concern over the effectiveness of psychological debriefings arose in the relevant literature with the publication of two Australian studies. McFarlane (1988) reported on the longitudinal course of posttraumatic morbidity in the wake of bush fires. One aspect of the study found that acute posttraumatic stress was predicted by avoidance of thinking about problems and property loss, and not attending undefined forms of psychological debriefings. Chronic variations of posttraumatic stress disorder were best predicted by premorbid, non-event related factors, such as a family history of psychiatric disorders, concurrent avoidance and neuroticism, and a tendency not to confront conflicts. Finally, the study found that delayed onset posttraumatic stress developed in individuals who not only had higher premorbid neuroticism scores and greater property loss, but also attended the undefined debriefings. While these factors, when submitted to discriminant function analysis, only resulted in the correct identification of 53% of the delayed onset group, this study is often reported as evidence for lack of effectiveness of debriefings. The lack of an operational definition of debriefing, combined with significant interaction effects, makes such a univariate conclusion unfounded.

The second of the early negative outcome studies was that of Kenardy and colleagues (1996). Kenardy's investigation purported to assess the effectiveness of stress debriefings for 62 "debriefed helpers" compared to 133 who were apparently not debriefed subsequent to an earthquake in New Castle, Australia. This study is often cited as evidence for the ineffectiveness of debriefings, yet the authors state, "we were not able to influence the availability or nature of the debriefing . . ." (p. 39). They continue, "It was assumed that all subjects in this study who reported having been debriefed did in fact receive posttrauma debriefing. However, there was no standardization of debriefing services. . ." (p.47). These rather remarkable epistemological revelations by the authors serve as evidence that no conclusion can be reached as to the effectiveness of an intervention (debriefing), the nature and even the existence of which was unknown. Yet such fatal flaws have failed to deter critics of the "debriefing" process, whatever the term may mean.

Unfortunately, those who cite these two investigations as "evidence" of the lack of effectiveness of "psychological debriefings" appear to have neglected the immutable empirical reality that failure to insure the standardization and reliability of the independent variable (debriefing) renders the results of the investigations unintelligible, ungeneralizable, and certainly not supportive of the null hypothesis, as some would contend. The sine qua non of research is internal validity; unfortunately, these studies possess no such validity as it pertains to the evaluation of the effectiveness of CISD, as the term is being used herein.

Perhaps the primary scientific foundation for the "debate" over early intervention, especially "debriefing," can be found in the Cochrane Library's s. Citing as evidence the results of the Cochrane Library Review (Wessely, Rose, & Bisson, 1998; Rose, Bisson, & Wessely, 2002) and selected derivative reviews (Litz et al., 2002; van Emmerick et al., 2002), some have reached the conclusion that early psychological intervention (especially "debriefing") is ineffectual and may cause harm to some. A few individuals have even suggested that early intervention after disasters and mass violence should be discontinued.

These reviews are held out to be methodologically robust because they rely most heavily upon investigations using randomization, i.e., randomized controlled trials (RCTs). The primary Cochrane constituents are discussed below.

Bisson, Jenkins, Alexander, and Bannister (1997) randomly assigned 110 patients with severe burns to either a "debriefing" group or a control group. The clinical standard *group* debriefing was abandoned for an *individual* adaptation. A serious design flaw emerged as the goal of randomization, i.e., equivalent group memberships, was not met. The group of "debriefed" individuals had more severe burns and greater financial problems than the non-debriefed group of individuals, thus direct comparison was inappropriate. It is important to note that both of these variables were later associated with poorer outcome on post test; that is, on post test, the "debriefed" group had more severe traumatic stress scores at 13 months. The authors concede, however, the differences between groups at pretest were "associated more strongly with poorer outcome as measured by the IES at 13 months than were [debriefing] status" (p.79). Despite the lack of equivalent groups and the failure to follow standard clinical protocols for *group* debriefings, these authors contend that the results cast serious doubt upon the utility of debriefings.

Hobbs, Mayou, Harrison, and Warlock (1996) performed a randomized trial of debriefings for 106 (54 debriefed; 52 control) motor vehicle accident victims. Once again randomization failed to achieve equivalent groups for comparison in that the individuals who were debriefed had more severe injuries and spent more days in the hospital at pretest compared to the control group. Both factors predicted poorer psychological outcome at post test. Similarly, the clinical standard *group* process was abandoned so as to employ individual debriefings. The individuals receiving the debriefings had higher traumatic stress scores at follow-up. Even more interesting, these data have been used to argue that debriefing may be injurious. Yet, close scrutiny reveals the actual traumatic stress scores were not in a clinical range (indicative of significant distress) at *any* time, and the overall change from 15.13 to 15.97 (clinical ranges begin at approximately 26) has no clinical significance whatsoever.

In a 4-year longitudinal follow-up investigation, Mayou, Ehlers, and Hobbs (2000) found the intervention group (individualized debriefings) remained symptomatic. Once again, however, the *group* debriefing process was not used, and the debriefing was used in a stand-alone manner (contrary to a multi-component prescription including follow-up).

It seems a non-sequitur to conclude on the basis of these three oft-cited studies that psychological debriefing is ineffective or, worse yet, harmful when the debriefing process was individualized, as opposed to the group format; when the debriefing was taken out of its prescribed multi-component context; and when it was applied to medical patients with unresolved medical complaints. The internal validity of these investigations seems suspect at best; further, it seems impossible to generalize from these studies to any other debriefing protocols (Tuckey, 2007).

In other Cochrane-cited studies, Lee, Slade, and Lygo (1996) assessed the effectiveness of individual debriefing on women following miscarriages. No significant changes were attributed to debriefings. In a more recent variation, Small and colleagues (2000) used "debriefing" subsequent to operative childbirth (Caesarean, forceps, or vacuum delivery). Once again individual debriefing was employed, as opposed to group debriefing. The debriefing took place prior to hospital discharge, while the psychological assessment took place at six months post-childbirth. Unfortunately, the debriefing process, as operationalized in this study, was not specifically described. The reported results indicated that 94% of the women in the debriefing group found the debriefing either "helpful" or "very helpful" ($n = 437/463$). The intervention was found to be ineffective on the targeted symptoms of depression, as would be predicted, in that debriefing is not a substitute for psychotherapy. Nevertheless, the authors surprisingly conclude this study fails to support the utility of debriefings.

Two studies seldom mentioned yielded different results, however. Bordow and Porritt (1979) assessed the effectiveness of a multi-component, -like crisis intervention on three groups of motor vehicle accident victims. The control group received no intervention, the second group received a one-session individual assessment/intervention, while the third group received the same as the second group plus 2 to 10 hours of crisis intervention. Results indicated a positive dose-response relationship with intervention. Bunn and Clarke (1979) conducted an experimental evaluation of brief intervention on anxiety symptoms for the relatives of seriously ill hospital patients. The intervention consisted of about 20 minutes of crisis counseling in which subjects received information, psychological support, and an opportunity to vent. Subjects were randomly assigned to experimental and control conditions. Results were supportive of the assumption that brief crisis counseling is an effective anxiolytic.

In retrospect, rather than support the notion that group debriefings are ineffectual and potentially harmful, these data would appear to support a very different set of conclusions. First, these studies would appear to support the conclusion that clinicians should use caution implementing a group crisis intervention protocol with individuals singularly (Busuttil & Busuttil, 1995). Obviously, none of the therapeutic elements of group process (Yalom, 1970) are available to be used when a group protocol is employed one patient at a time. This would appear similar to attempting group psychotherapy protocols with individual psychotherapy patients. Secondly, these findings would suggest caution with the use of individualized psychological crisis intervention tactics with primary medical patients within minimal temporal distance from their medical stressors, or with primary medical patients with ongoing unresolved medical stressors. Turnbull, Busuttil, and Pittman (1997) argue, and Mitchell (1983) would concur, such applications are inappropriate due to the timing of the intervention and the nature of the patients' crisis event or trauma. As a crisis intervention tactic, group debriefing is best suited for acute situational crisis responses. Furthermore, debriefings are certainly not a substitute for psychotherapy, psychotropic medication, analgesics, or psychological rehabilitation. Thirdly, the studies which used debriefing absent a positive outcome appeared to use the debriefing as a stand-alone intervention, outside of the prescribed multi-faceted -like context (Everly & Mitchell, 1999). Kraus (1997) argues that debriefing should not be a stand-alone intervention, in agreement with Everly and Mitchell (1999) and the British Psychological Society (1990). Fourth, given these admonitions, these findings appear to support the implementation of individual crisis counseling (Bunn & Clarke, 1979) and multi-component interventions (Bordow & Porritt, 1979). Unfortunately, no conclusions regarding group debriefings, in general, or CISD, in specific, can be made from these data (Everly & Mitchell, 1999; Robinson & Mitchell, 1995; Dyregrov, 1998).

To paraphrase the philosopher/psychologist William James, "To disprove the assertion that all crows are black, one need only find one crow that is white!" Therefore, to disprove the assertion that all debriefings are ineffectual, one need only find one debriefing that is effective! In support of debriefings, but specifically the CISD model of group psychological crisis intervention, we find several investigations: Robinson and Mitchell (1993, 1995), with emergency medical services personnel; Nurmi (1999), with rescue personnel in the wake of the sinking of the Estonia; Wee and colleagues (1999), with emergency medical technicians subsequent to the Los Angeles riots; Bohl (1991), with police; Chemtob and colleagues (1997), with healthcare providers subsequent to Hurricane Iniki; Jenkins (1996), with emergency medical personnel in the wake of a mass shooting; Campfield and Hills (2001), with bank robbery victims; and Deahl et al. (2000) and Hoge et al. (2006), with military personnel [see Chapter Seven for details on these studies]. All of these investigations offer varying degrees of evidence for the effectiveness of the CISD intervention. In each of the studies cited, emergency services or other healthcare personnel were the recipients of the CISD intervention. Some of these studies, however, may be criticized for their lack of randomized subject assignment. However, four of the aforementioned studies possessed a static control condition, while one possessed a time-lagged control. These research designs are known to be vulnerable to selection, mortality, and maturation as threats to internal validity and vulnerable to the selection-intervention interaction threat to external validity (Campbell &

Stanley,1963). The studies by Campfield and Hills (2001), Deahl and colleagues (2000), and Hoge et al. (2006) were indeed randomized controlled trials. Furthermore, in order to partially compensate for the vulnerabilities and derive greater insight from their collective findings, Everly and Boyle (1999) subsequently meta-analyzed studies wherein the CISD group crisis intervention was utilized with emergency services personnel (as originally intended by Mitchell). Each of the five investigations utilized control conditions, but none used randomized assignment. Perhaps the greatest singular value of randomization is the protection against systematic experimental error. One of the advantages of meta-analysis is that through combining investigations of diverse investigators using diverse subject populations in diverse naturalistic settings, the researcher is provided a large subject pool that is minimally vulnerable to systematic error, i.e., a similar goal as randomization. The results of the meta-analysis found evidence suggesting that the CISD is, indeed, clinically effective across applications with a reported Cohen's d in excess of .8 (Everly & Boyle, 1999).

In sum, experimental generalizability, i.e., forming conclusions about one set of independent variables tested within an initial investigatory process on the basis of another independent set of investigations, is predicated upon the achievement of at least five criteria (see van der Veer, van Ijzendoorn, & Valsinor, 1994; Rossi & Freeman, 1984): 1) first and foremost, it is essential that the replication utilize the same independent variable(s) that were used in the initial investigation, this operational fidelity is the sine qua non of validity for any given replication; 2) replicability of relevant dependent variables is also an essential aspect of replicability; 3) replicability of comparable research venues or the overall investigatory milieu (e.g., comparable mass disaster settings) is often a challenging but necessary aspect of replication; 4) those performing the intervention should have demonstrated clinical competency and comparable levels of training plus implementation skill when compared to those in the initial investigation; and finally, 5) subject/ target populations should be in the replication when compared to the initial investigation (e.g., in a replication of a disaster mental health study, the replication should use only survivors of mass disasters). While it is generally accepted that replicability is an important aspect of science, the replicatory process must demonstrate external validation as operationally enumerated above. Said more cogently, the intervention programs used in the replication "must be faithful reproductions of the programs...in order for the impact assessment [replication] to be relevant" (Rossi & Freeman, 1985).

The attempt to obtain experimental generalizability from the s to the practice of early intervention subsequent to disasters and mass violence clearly fails the test of operational fidelity. The environment associated with medical/ surgical procedures (even burns and accidents) is quite different than the environment associated with disasters and mass violence. The early interventions, as defined within the Cochrane studies consisting of one-time individual counseling sessions, are quite different than crisis intervention groups (critical incident stress debriefing) and the more recently prescribed phasic, integrated, multi-component intervention system (e.g., Critical Incident Stress Management). In addition, the issues of clinical competency and training have been virtually ignored, a serious omission for those who are concerned with the quality of crisis intervention and emergency mental health response (Dyregrov, 1998, 1999). Finally, the subjects within the Cochrane studies are largely medical/surgical/obstetric patients and as such are very different than primary survivors of mass disaster and/or emergency services personnel. Kagan (1988) has noted that if the mechanisms (independent variables) mediating the observations (dependent variables) are different from the initial investigation to the replication, the same conceptual term (e.g., "debriefing") should not be used to describe both.

SUMMARY AND RECOMMENDATIONS

Recalling the research investigations reviewed in this chapter, a trend clearly emerges that may serve as the best summary of both the lexical as well as substantive issues in the field at this point in time.

We shall conclude this chapter with a summary of that trend with subsequent recommendations:

- **Problem: The term "debriefing" has been an ill-defined and often unspecified intervention.** The early first generation of "debriefing" studies (McFarlane, 1988; Kenardy et al., 1996) could not define the term debriefing, nor could they describe what actually happened, if anything, during the debriefing. Their contribution to our understanding of debriefing is to underscore the need to verify the nature and existence of the intervention.

- **Problem: The use of the term "debriefing" to mean individual counseling and individual early intervention with medical patients is inconsistent with extant applications in crisis and disaster mental health intervention.** This second generation of "debriefing" studies was conducted with medical patients using an individualized intervention format (Bisson et al., 1997; Hobbs et al., 1996; Mayou, Ehlers, & Hobbs, 2000; Lee, Slade, & Lygo, 1996; Small et al., 2000). Their contribution to our understanding of debriefing is that a) crisis intervention is clearly not a substitute for psychotherapy, but may be very helpful nevertheless (Small et al., 2000), b) crisis intervention is probably not suitable for patients in acute medical distress because it is not a substitute for analgesia, physical rehabilitation, psychological rehabilitation, reconstructive surgery, or financial counseling. These studies have also clearly shown that it is premature to reach any adverse conclusions with regard to debriefings (Bisson, McFarlane, & Rose, 2000).

- **Problem: Campbell and Stanley (1963) in their classic monograph point out that when randomization fails to attain equivalent groups at the pretreatment stage, the experiment is no longer considered a true experimental design.** Yet some continue to embrace three investigations which failed to achieve random allocation as "evidence" that "debriefings" are harmful. This, even though the authors of the most recent of psychological debriefing themselves (Rose, Bisson, Wessely, 2002), although calling for a cessation of "compulsory debriefings pending further evidence" (p. 10) have concluded, "We are unable to comment on the use of group debriefing, nor the use of debriefing after mass traumas" (p.10).

- **Recommendations: Tuckey (2007) has enumerated seven issues that must be addressed in order to move toward a resolution of the "debriefing debate."**
  - Use random allocation to intervention and control conditions.
  - Baseline measures should be used in order to ensure that random allocation achieves equal groups and to provide potential for an intra-group analysis.
  - Clearly define and homogenize the trauma exposure.
  - Employ a standardized debriefing intervention wherein the interventionists are well trained and the integrity of the intervention is assessed.
  - Choose outcome variables that are relevant and meaningful at multiple points.
  - Maximize response rates and assess responders vs. non-responders on key moderator variables in order to assess potential response bias.
  - In reporting the research outcome, care should be

taken to provide full disclosure as to procedures surrounding the independent and dependent variables (so that the study can be fully replicated); full disclosure should be made as to the critical incident (trauma), subjects, intervention procedure, data collection, and statistical analysis so as to elucidate the potential for moderator variables or alternative sources of effect.

In commenting on Tuckey's analysis of the debriefing debate, Robinson (2007) alludes to the plethora of methodological flaws that haunt this field and have done so for 20 years. She acknowledges Tuckey's contribution by noting, "This disciplined approach has enabled delineation of flaws in the data as well as conclusions drawn on the basis of findings. The author uses her analysis of 'what not to do' when you are conducting research in this area to develop research guidelines on what should be done" (p. 121).

- **Recommendations: Bisson, Brayne, Ochberg, and Everly (2007) have formulated a set of guidelines designed to further assist the field in moving forward**. Among their recommendations are the following.
    - Shortly after a traumatic event, it is important that those affected be provided, in an empathic manner, with practical, pragmatic psychological support.
    - It is important that provisions be made for individuals to obtain the appropriate early support after a traumatic event. However, any early intervention approach should be based on an accurate and current assessment of need.
    - Individuals who experience continued symptoms a month or more after a traumatic event can benefit from psychological intervention. If an individual's reaction is extreme, formal intervention can be

beneficial when applied earlier.
- We encourage exploration of a psychological first aid approach that takes explicit account of people's natural resilience (Bisson, Brayne, Ochberg, & Everly, 2007, 1018-1019).

There does exist a corpus of data regarding the small group crisis intervention, Critical Incident Stress Debriefing (CISD). This third generation of debriefing studies employed the CISD model of group-format debriefing (Mitchell & Everly, 1997). These studies conducted by Nurmi (1999), Bohl (1991), Chemtob et al. (1997), Wee et al. (1999), Jenkins (1996), Everly, Boyle, and Lating (1999) in a meta-analytic investigation, and randomized studies conducted by Deahl, et al. (2000) with British military, Hoge, Castro, McGurk, et al. (2006) with American military, and Campfield and Hill (2001) with bank robbery victims clearly support the assertion that the CISD model of "debriefing" can be an effective clinical tool for reducing psychological distress, reducing alcohol use, and in mitigating post traumatic distress. Their contribution to our understanding of "debriefing" is demonstrating the value of a standardized, theoretically based, empirically developed protocol for small group crisis intervention.

Finally, Deahl (2000) states, "The effectiveness of acute interventions to prevent PTSD…has become increasingly politicised and more than a matter of science" (p. 931). Dyregrov (1998) states, "In my opinion the debate on debriefing is not only a scientific but also a political debate. It entails power and positions in the therapeutic world…[debriefing] represented a threat to the psychiatric professional elite…many people being trained in the technique were peer support personnel and mental health workers outside psychiatric institutions. [Debriefing] thus has been partly self-help and consumer driven where the recipients of services have had more control than in traditional academic or medical approaches…"(p. 7).

CHAPTER NINE

Strategic Planning

Sun Tzu, the great Chinese general and military strategist (c. 544 – 496 BC), wrote the classic military text *The Art of War.* Therein he noted, "Strategy without tactics is the slowest route to victory. Tactics without strategy is the noise before defeat."

The nascent field of disaster mental health has often been a field plagued by the vigorous pursuit of tactics, while often ignoring the importance of having a strategic formulation within which the tactics may reside. Indeed, the perfectly performed tactical intervention implemented at the wrong time can be as complete a failure as the tactical intervention performed inadequately. Thus, while tactical proficiency (how to intervene) is essential, so is the strategic understanding of when and where to implement the chosen interventions in order to best achieve the objective. We recall the foundations of integrative crisis intervention and disaster mental health being grounded in Millon's formulations. Integrative crisis intervention and disaster mental health may be thought of as the implementation of an integrated array of interventions concurrently combined and catalytically sequenced in such a manner as to best respond to the unique needs, or "idiographic heterogeneity," of a given person or group of persons. According to Millon, Grossman, Meagher, Millon, and Everly (1999), "The palette of methods and techniques available to the therapist must be commensurate with the idiographic heterogeneity of the patient for whom the methods and techniques are intended" (1999, p. 145). This is true for the crisis interventionist and person in crisis as well.

According to Flynn (2003), "There seems to be a consensus that the process of planning is nearly as important as the content of the plans. Individual and organizational relationships among interested parties are formed and solidified, planning responsibilities of the SMHA [state mental health agencies] and others are established, and multiple plans are integrated during the process" (p. 6). In this chapter we shall take a closer look at strategic planning.

A STRATEGIC PLANNING MODEL: THREAT-TARGET-TYPE-TIMING-RESOURCES

Carville and Begala (2002) explained that there are three essential elements in planning: objectives, strategies, and tactics. **Objectives** are the overarching goals. The **strategy** is the plan of action. **Tactics** are the specific steps and tools used to implement strategic plan and to achieve the goal.

The goal in psychological crisis intervention and disaster mental health response is to prevent and/or reduce human distress

The strategy is the specific planning formula employed. Below we have provided a simple strategic planning model based on McCabe, and colleagues (2004).

1. *Threat* designation. This step entails the identification of the specific threats most likely to be encountered by the community, organization, and institution. Intervention plans must be threat-specific. For example, a town meeting in the wake of a hurricane may be recommended, whereas, in the wake of a pandemic it could be fatal.

2. For each threat, the *target*, or constituent group to be protected or served, is designated and carefully defined.

3. The third step in formulating the tactical response plan entails

the stipulation of what *types of interventions* are to be used for each target group. These interventions may be thought of as a type of "tool kit" consisting of the various tactical interventions. Earlier, in Chapter Five, we listed and described the "toolkit." Table 5.1 could be a useful aid in planning the utilization of specific tactical interventions. From a broader perspective, tactical proficiencies may be referred to as *core tactical competencies*. Later in this chapter, we shall review thoughts on core competencies.

4. The *timing* of implementing interventions is essential. Disasters evolve in somewhat predictable stages, and interventions are most likely to be successful when they are applied at a point in the evolution of the disaster when they are most likely to exert their greatest effect. Similarly, applying interventions at inappropriate temporal points could easily neutralize any potential benefit and even intensify distress.

5. Having completed steps 1 through 4, an *inventory of resources* is necessary to plan the tactical response.

6. The *assessment of tactical competency and capability* as represented by the identified resources is the next step in the plan formulation.

7. Finally, if areas of deficiency are identified, *tactical training* is required to meet the core tactical competencies as identified above. Furthermore, conducting training updates and periodic simulations and table-top exercises is an essential aspect of effective training.

TOWARD BEST PRACTICES AND CORE COMPETENCIES

In this section, we shall review suggestions on the psychosocial response to crisis and disaster from various sources. The reader will see certain commonalities emerge.

In August of 2002, the World Psychiatric Association meeting featured a plenary session by its president Juan Lopez-Ibor on the topic of disaster mental health. Lopez-Ibor (2002) asserted that certain principles of intervention were important. Among them, he noted the following:

- Intervention should be as immediate as possible.
- Mental health intervention should be integrated with physical health intervention.
- Intervention should focus on entire populations, not just primary victims.
- Assessment and triage are important elements.
- Verbal intervention is important; debriefings, discussions, and social support both individually and in groups.
- The stigma associated with seeking treatment should be reduced.
- The provision of adequate information is important.
- Sensitivity to situational and cultural diversity should be emphasized.
- Pre-incident training is important.
- Finally, the role of the mental health professional should be to integrate the social, biological, and systems response to disasters.

National Institute of Mental Health (NIMH)

In September of 2002, the National Institute of Mental Health published its recommendations on mental health and mass violence (NIMH, 2002). Some of the key points are summarized below.

- Early intervention will be defined as being within 4 weeks of the incident or mass disaster.
- Expect normal recovery from the majority of those initially affected.
- Mental health services should be integrated within the overall disaster response plan.

- Receiving intervention should be voluntary.
- Intervention itself should be structured within a hierarchy designed to meet basic needs first (survival, safety, shelter, physical health, food, psychological health, communications).
- The key elements of early intervention were deemed to be: pre-incident preparation, psychological first aid, needs assessment and monitoring, outreach and information dissemination, technical assistance, fostering resiliency and natural recovery mechanisms, triage, treatment (cognitive behavioral therapy was believed to show significant potential).
- There should be a sensitivity to diversity (cultural, occupational), with intervention provided on an "as needed" basis.
- There is limited research on mass disaster mental health. Nevertheless, cognitive and behavioral interventions show promise. Stand-alone, one-on-one recitals of incident-related facts alone without follow-up does not show any evidence of reducing risk and may be disruptive to recovery mechanisms. A new nomenclature is needed, e.g., the term "debriefing" is too generic and has lost functional utility.
- Clinical research needs to be conducted.
- Interventions should be based upon defensible empiricism.
- The providers of early psychological intervention can include mental health professionals, medical professionals, the clergy, school personnel, emergency responders, and community volunteers operating within a sanctioned system, e.g., an incident command system. Specialized training is recommended.
- No timetable for post-incident follow-up exists, however, it is expected that survivors without symptoms after 2 months will generally not require follow-up. On the other hand, follow-up should be offered to those with acute stress disorder or pre-existing psychiatric problems, the bereaved, those

requiring medical or surgical intervention, those at high risk because of intense or chronic exposure, and those who request follow-up.[Note: The interested reader should refer to the original NIMH (2002) report.]

Employee Assistance Professional Association (EAPA)

In October of 2002, the Employee Assistance Professional Association released the results of its Disaster Preparedness Task Force (EAPA, 2002). The major recommendations from this organization, which serves the mental health needs of the business and industrial sectors, are listed below.

- Disasters affect the workplace. As a result, the employee assistance professional can play a role in assisting the employee and the organization.
- The employee assistance professional can assist the organization in developing a disaster response plan.
- Critical incident and disaster response should be configured as a continuum of services consisting of pre-incident contingency planning, acute response, post-incident response, follow-up, and response review/plan revision.
- Pre-incident contingency planning should consist of risk assessment, policy development, management consultation marketing, supervisory training, disaster preparedness, critical incident stress management training, and collaboration.
- Acute response intervention should consist of on-site response, coordination of response services, collaboration, logistical and technical support, and management consultation.
- Post-incident response should consist of psychological defusings, group critical incident stress debriefings, large group crisis management briefings (company "town meetings"), assessment and referral services, and self-care for interventionists.

- Follow-up services should consist of management briefings, disaster reviews, data collection and analysis, and training.
- The response review and disaster plan revision should entail examining policies and procedures in light of lessons learned from the most recent incident. New disaster plans should be designed if necessary and new training should be implemented if needed. Research is encouraged.

National Voluntary Organizations Active in Disasters (NVOAD)

In January 2003, the National Voluntary Organizations Active in Disasters (NVOAD) convened a gathering of organizations that provide training in crisis intervention and disaster mental health (referred to as *early psychological intervention*, or EPI). In the spirit of the NVOAD "Four C's" (Cooperation, Communication, Coordination, and Collaboration), the American Red Cross, the International Critical Incident Stress Foundation, National Organization for Victims Assistance, and the Salvation Army came together to learn what each organization does, how to promote shared practices and communications, and increase collaboration and partnership throughout their networks and stakeholders. In May of 2005, NVOAD released a consensus report. The main points are listed below.

Points of Consensus:
1. Early Psychological Intervention (EPI) is valued.
2. EPI is a multi-component system to meet the needs of those impacted.
3. Specialized training in early psychological intervention is necessary.
4. EPI is one point on a continuum of psychological care. This spectrum ranges from pre-incident preparedness to post-incident psychotherapy, when needed.
5. Cooperation, communication, coordination and collaboration are essential to the delivery of EPI.

Elaboration of the 5 Points of Consensus:

1. Early Psychological Intervention (EPI) is valued.
   - EPI refers to a body of psychological interventions designed to mitigate acute distress while not interfering with natural recovery processes.
   - Where there is a need for physical disaster response services, there is a potential need for psychological disaster services.
   - EPI is a valuable contribution along the continuum of disaster response services.
   - EPI is not psychotherapy, nor is it a substitute for psychotherapy.

2. Early psychological intervention is a multi-component system designed to meet the needs of those impacted. Specific early psychological interventions should be included in any disaster response initiative. A list of these interventions includes but is not limited to those below.
   - Pre-incident training
   - Incident assessment and strategic planning
   - Risk and crisis communication
   - Acute psychological assessment and triage
   - Crisis intervention with large groups
   - Crisis intervention with small groups
   - Crisis intervention with individuals, face-to-face and hotlines
   - Crisis planning and intervention with communities
   - Crisis planning and intervention with organizations
   - Psychological first aid
   - Facilitating access to appropriate levels of care when needed
   - Assisting special and diverse populations

- Spiritual assessment and care
- Self-care and family care, including safety and security
- Post-incident evaluation and training based on lessons learned

3. Specialized training in EPI is necessary.
    - Fundamental understanding of National Incident Management System (NIMS) and Incident Command System (ICS) - reporting relationships; how EPI fits within disaster response operations; collaborative relationships; accountability for deployment
    - Pre-incident training
    - Incident assessment and strategic planning
    - Risk and crisis communication
    - Acute psychological assessment and triage
    - Crisis intervention with large groups
    - Crisis intervention with small groups
    - Crisis intervention with individuals, face-to-face and hotlines
    - Crisis planning and intervention with communities
    - Crisis planning and intervention with organizations
    - Psychological first aid
    - Facilitating access to appropriate levels of care when needed
    - Assisting special and diverse populations
    - Spiritual assessment and care
    - Self-care and family care, including safety and security
    - Post-incident evaluation and training based on lessons learned
    - Commitment to ongoing continued education and training, team/organizational involvement

4. Early psychological intervention is one point on a continuum of psychological care. This spectrum ranges from pre-incident preparedness to post-incident psychotherapy, when needed. In concert with numberous organizations cited throughout this volume, the NVOAD community enthusiastically endorsed the notion of disaster mental health services being provided within an integrated, multi-component system. Ideally, mental health services should be seamlessly integrated with physical health services.

5. The fifth point of consensus represents a reiteration of the principles upon which all NVOAD services are based. The importance of cooperation, communication, coordination, and collaboration is inherent in the delivery of all disaster relief services.

Law Enforcement Survey

Sheehan, Everly, and Langlieb (2004) reported the results of a survey of law enforcement organizations active in disaster and uniquely challenging critical incidents. Among the organizations surveyed were U.S. Bureau of Alcohol, Tobacco, and Forearms (ATF), U.S. Secret Service, U.S. Marshals Service, Federal Bureau of Investigation (FBI), Federal Law Enforcement Training Center (FLETC) and others.

They recognized the importance and the value of early psychological intervention/ critical incident response. They all endorsed the utilization of a phase-sensitive, multi-component crisis intervention system as part of an overall continuum of care. Specific tactical interventions, in most programs, included the ability to perform 1:1 crisis intervention, small group crisis intervention, large group crisis intervention, and family support services, as well as the ability to access spiritual support services and treatment services.

Centers for Disease Control and Prevention (CDC) and the Association of Schools of Public Health (ASPH)

Everly, Beaton, Pfefferbaum, and Parker (in press) reported on the CDC/ASPH recommendations for the development of proposed core competencies in disaster mental health.

In 2000, the Centers for Disease Control and Prevention (CDC) and the Association of Schools of Public Health (ASPH) established the Centers for Public Health Preparedness (CPHP) to educate and train the public health workforce to prepare for and respond to acts of domestic terrorism, as well as other disasters that might threaten the public health and welfare of the United States. In 2004, CDC and ASPH directed CPHP network members to create the CPHP Mental Health and Psychosocial Preparedness Exemplar Group to address the mental health aspects of terrorism and mass disasters. The CPHP Mental Health and Psychosocial Preparedness Exemplar Group was transitioned into the Disaster Mental Health Collaborative Group in 2006. The resulting consensus document containing five core competencies in disaster mental health is excerpted below (Everly, Beaton, Pfefferbaum, & Parker, in press).

Proposed consensus core competencies in disaster mental health

Preamble: The following represents the consensus core competencies for disaster mental, psychosocial, and behavioral health preparedness and response. These competencies can serve as a framework for the development of training programs, educational curricula, evaluation processes, and organizational and human development initiatives, such as job descriptions and performance evaluations. These competencies must be integrated within organizational structure and incident management systems and are guided by the following principles of adherence to performance within one's scope of practice, consideration of the context of the situation, sensitivity to diversity and cultural competence, recognition of the desire to reduce the risk of any harm that may come from intervention, and recognition of the importance of teamwork and adherence to the incident command system.

Consensus core competencies in disaster mental health

- Disaster response personnel will demonstrate the ability to define and/or describe key terms and concepts related to disaster mental/psychoscoial/behavioral health preparedness and response.
- Disaster response personnel will demonstrate skills needed to communicate effectively.
- Disaster response personnel will demonstrate skill in assessing the need for, and type of, intervention (if any).
- Disaster response personnel will demonstrate skill in developing and implementing an action plan (based upon one's knowledge, skill, authority, and functional role) to meet those needs identified through assessment.
- Disaster response personnel will demonstrate skill in caring for responder peers and self.

A WORD OF CAUTION

Relatively recently, as noted in earlier chapters, the endeavor of providing psychological crisis intervention has been re-examined. Some have even called for an end to early intervention due to concern over potential iatrogenic harm as a result of crisis intervention, especially the ill-defined "psychological debriefing." Concern over possible harm resulting from crisis intervention is a valid concern. "Clearly, however, in light of research suggesting that crisis intervention can exert positive effects, efforts should be directed toward identifying mechanisms of therapeutic effect, potential sources of adverse iatrogenesis, and compensatory strategies developed to respond to the latter" (Everly, 2003, p. 180). It would seem that such is a superior course as opposed to adopting reductionistic binary thinking wherein we view, and therefore subsequently judge, crisis intervention to be "all good" or "all bad." It seems that we would want to avoid a condition wherein we "throw the baby out with the bathwater."

In Chapter Six, we reviewed putative mechanisms of therapeutic effect. Here, we provide cautionary guidance on the practice of crisis intervention and disaster mental health.

- It is imperative that emergent intervention follow the basic principles and hierarchy of needs, i.e., meeting basic needs first. More specifically, needs for food, water, shelter, alleviation of pain, reunification with family members, and the provision of a sense of safety and security should all precede the utilization of psychologically-oriented crisis interventions.

- Group crisis intervention poses a risk for iatrogenic harm if it introduces traumatogenetic material to group members who would not otherwise be exposed to such material. To reduce this risk, it is suggested that small crisis intervention groups be made up of naturally occurring cohorts and/or homogeneous groups with regard to trauma exposure and toxicity. The formation of small *heterogeneous* crisis intervention debriefings should not be endorsed.

- It has been proposed that health education regarding signs and symptoms of distress may actually psychogenically create such symptoms in highly suggestible persons. It is hard to accept this notion of potential mass hysteria so as to "keep information from people for their own good." Nevertheless, it may be argued that the manner in which the information is presented may have a significant effect upon subsequent hysterical symptomatology. Such information should be presented as basic health education-related information designed to empower the recipients of such information to assume more, not less, control in responding to adversity, when such seems appropriate.

- The notion of the value of cathartic ventilation has been challenged to the degree that concern has been expressed that cathartic ventilation may become a pathogenic abreactive process. To reduce this risk, it might be suggested that assessment and triage are essential elements of effective crisis intervention wherein psychologically vulnerable or brittle persons (highly aroused, morbidly depressed, highly guilt-ridden individuals, the intensely bereaved, dissociating individuals, those experiencing psychotic symptomatology, those physically injured or in pain) not be included in group crisis intervention. Rather, they should be approached individually and more appropriate interventions should be utilized. Furthermore, whether individually or in groups, deep probing techniques, psychotherapeutic interpretation, and paradoxical intention should clearly be avoided.

- Concern has been expressed that crisis intervention techniques should never consist of univariate stand-alone interventions. Rather, crisis intervention should consist of a phase-sensitive, multi-variate intervention system.

- So that crisis intervention is not conceived of as a substitute for more formal psychotherapeutic and/or psychiatric interventions, crisis intervention is conceived of as but one point on a continuum of care that certainly includes psychotherapy. The natural corollary of this conceptualization is that successful crisis intervention, similar to successful physical first aid, may actually consist of simply facilitating access to the next and more appropriate level of care.

- Lastly, it is essential that those practicing psychological crisis intervention receive specialized training to do so (Dyregrov,

1999; Stapleton et al., 2006). Standard counseling and psychotherapy training will typically prove inadequate to respond effectively to mass disasters, large-scale violence, terrorism, and even well circumscribed acute crises.

SUMMARY

It is clear that the state of the art recommendations for emergency mental health response in the wake of trauma and mass disaster emphasize the need for a phasic, integrated, multi-component crisis intervention system. Consistent with the notion of integrative psychotherapy, crisis intervention should be integrative; that is, crisis intervention should be conceived of as a strategic configurational system of tactics in which each intervention technique is selected not only for its efficacy in resolving singular clinical and pre-clinical features but also for its contribution to the overall constellation of intervention procedures in their task of responding to the unique demands of any given circumstance. In order to be most effective, the components of such a system must be employed not only with tactical proficiency and skill but also with strategic insight. Organizations such as the American Red Cross, the Salvation Army, the National Organization for Victim's Assistance, the U. S. Coast Guard, the U.S. National Guard, the U.S. Bureau of Alcohol, Tobacco, and Firearms, the International Critical Incident Stress Foundation, the U.S. Marshals' service, and the Employee Assistance Professionals Association either utilize and/or recommend such integrated, multi-component crisis intervention systems.

PART THREE

Applications

CHAPTER TEN

Individual Crisis Intervention: Psychological First Aid & SAFER-R

Most authorities agree that the practice of mental health is replete with acute crises and that large scale disasters leave in their wake a need for some form of acute mental health services. However, a review of current literature on crisis intervention and disaster mental health, as has been noted earlier, reveals differing points of view on the methods that should be employed (Raphael, 1986; NIMH, 2002). Nevertheless, there appears to be virtual universal endorsement, by relevant authorities, of the value of acute "psychological first aid" (PFA; American Psychiatric Association, 1954; DHHS, 2004; Raphael, 1986; NIMH, 2002; Institute of Medicine, 2003; WHO, 2003; Ritchie et al., 2004; Friedman et al., 2004).

HISTORICAL FOUNDATIONS OF PFA

In 1952, Thorne authored an editorial opinion on the nature of psychological first aid.

> "Without overemphasizing obvious analogies with medical first aid, it is immediately apparent that there are many acute situations in psychotherapy which truly constitute emergencies about which something should be effectively done…It appears that psychological first aid must utilize many of the older orthodox methods which are currently in disrepute with depth therapists because they operate

primarily only upon symptomatic levels. *Reassurance* is probably the first aid method par excellance...*Suggestion* can be used to deal with acute symptoms requiring immediate attention. *Catharsis* (or nondirective acceptance, reflection of feelings and clarification) may be mind-saving for people bursting over with acute tensions. *Persuasion, advice* and other supportive methods may help the client to deal with acute situational problems which are beyond his resources. Unfortunately many therapists have never learned to use these methods effectively..." (Thorne, 1952, p. 210).

In 1954, the American Psychiatric Association published the monograph entitled *Psychological First Aid in Community Disasters* (APA, 1954). That document therein defined and argued for the development of an acute mental health intervention referred to as "psychological first aid" (PFA). This early exposition noted, "In all disasters, whether they result from the forces of nature or from enemy attack, the people involved are subjected to stresses of a severity and quality not generally encountered...It is vital for all disaster workers to have some familiarity with common patterns of reaction to unusual emotional stress and strain. These workers must also know the fundamental principles of coping most effectively with disturbed people. Although [these suggestions have] been stimulated by the current needs for civil defense against possible enemy action... These principles are essential for those who are to help the victims of floods, fires, tornadoes, and other natural catastrophes" (APA, 1954, p. 5). This document delineated three important points:

- The constituents of PFA consist of the ability to recognize common (and one might assume uncommon) reactions post disaster;
- The constituents of PFA further consist of the fundamentals of coping; and

- That ALL disaster workers, not just mental health clinicians, should be trained.

In the first truly integrative disaster mental health text, *When Disaster Strikes*, Beverley Raphael noted, "…in the first hours after a disaster, at least 25% of the population may be stunned and dazed, apathetic and wandering—suffering from the disaster syndrome—especially if impact has been sudden and totally devastating…At this point, psychological first aid and triage…are necessary…" (Raphael, 1986, p.257). More recently, the Institute of Medicine (2003) has written, "In the past decade, there has been a growing movement in the world to develop a concept similar to physical first aid for coping with stressful and traumatic events in life. This strategy has been known by a number of names but is most commonly referred to as psychological first aid (PFA). Essentially, PFA provides individuals with skills they can use in responding to psychological consequences of [disasters] in their own lives, as well as in the lives of their family, friends, and neighbors. As a community program, it can provide a well-organized community task to increase skills, knowledge, and effectiveness in maximizing health and resiliency" (IOM, 2003, p. 4-5). Finally, W. Walter Menninger (2002), based upon the work of Karen Horney, has stated that the goal of psychological first aid is to reduce feelings of isolation, helplessness, and powerlessness.

The National Child Traumatic Stress Network and National Center for PTSD (2005), have collaborated and created an excellent program for PFA for mental health clinicians. It is available from related websites.

COMPONENTS OF PFA

PFA may be considered the earliest point on the psychological continuum of care. According to the Institute of Medicine (2003), "Psychological first aid is a group of skills identified to limit distress and negative health behaviors…PFA generally includes education about normal psychological responses to stressful and traumatic events; skills in active listening; understanding the importance of maintaining physical health and normal sleep, nutrition, and rest; and understanding when to seek help from professional caregivers" (IOM, 2003, p.7).

Raphael, in her seminal clinical treatise (1986) suggests that psychological first aid consists of the following:

- Comfort and consolation.
- Physical protection.
- Provision of physical necessities.
- Channeling energy into constructive behaviors.
- Reuniting victims with friends, family.
- Provision of behavioral and/or emotional support, especially during emotionally taxing tasks.
- Allowing emotional ventilation.
- Re-establishing a sense of security.
- Utilization of acute social and community support networks.
- Triage and referral for those in acute need.
- Referral to sub-acute and on-going support networks.

Raphael (1986) goes on to note that the provision of such acute psychological support is designed to achieve certain goals:

- Encouraging the "working through" process by reinforcing adaptive coping.
- Helping victims re-establish a sense of mastery (self-efficacy).
- Facilitating access to the next level of care, if necessary.
- Facilitating social reintegration.

Everly and Flynn (2005, 2006) attempted to provide further guidance into the nature of PFA by defining PFA and listing core behavioral elements:

- Assessment of need for intervention (level one assessment) [Note that the present use of the term "assessment" is not intended to refer to formal mental health assessment per se, rather, it is designed to refer more to an appraisal of functional psychological and behavioral status.]

- Stabilize – Subsequent to an initial assessment and determination that intervention of some form is warranted, act so as to prevent or reduce a worsening of the current psychological or behavioral status.
- Assess and triage (level two assessment) – Once initial stabilization has been achieved, further assessment is indicated with triage as a viable option. Assessment of functionality is the most essential aspect of this phase.
- Communicate – Communicate concern, reassurance, and information regarding stress management.
- Connect – Connect the person in distress to informal and/or formal support systems, if indicated.

The National Institute of Mental Health document, *Mental Health and Mass Violence* (2002), has enumerated the functions of psychological first aid as including the need to...

"Protect survivors from further harm,
Reduce physiological arousal,
Mobilize support for those who are most distressed,
Keep families together and facilitate reunions with loved ones,
Provide information and foster communication and education,
Use effective risk communication techniques" (p. 13).

The U. S. Department of Health and Human Services (DHHS, 2004) has compiled a list of "immediate mental health interventions." Within that list resides "psychological first aid." The components of psychological first aid include providing comfort, addressing immediate physical needs, supporting practical tasks, providing anticipatory information, listening and validating feeling, linking survivors to social support, normalizing stress reactions, and finally, reinforcing positive coping mechanisms.

The Inter-Agency Standing Committee (IASC) was established in 1992 in response to the United Nation's General Assembly Resolution 46/182. The resolution established the IASC as the primary mechanism for facilitating inter-agency decision-making in response to complex emergencies and natural disasters. In its guidelines for mental health response, the IASC specifically mentions PFA.

"Most individuals experiencing acute mental distress following exposure to extremely stressful events are best supported without medication. All aid workers, and especially health workers, should be able to provide very basic psychological first aid (PFa). PFa is often mistakenly seen as a clinical or emergency psychiatric intervention. Rather, it is a description of a humane, supportive response to a fellow human being who is suffering and who may need support. PFa encompasses:

- Protecting from further harm (in rare situations, very distressed persons may make decisions that put them at further risk of harm). Where appropriate, inform distressed survivors of their right to refuse to discuss the events with (other) aid workers or with journalists;
- Providing the opportunity for survivors to talk about the events, but without pressure. Respect the wish not to talk and avoid pushing for more information than the person may be ready to give;
- Listening patiently in an accepting and non-judgemental manner;
- Conveying genuine compassion;
- Identifying basic practical needs and ensuring that these are met;
- Asking for people's concerns and trying to address these;

- Discouraging negative ways of coping (specifically discouraging coping through use of alcohol and other substances, explaining that people in severe distress are at much higher risk of developing substance use problems);
- Encouraging participation in normal daily routines (if possible) and use of positive means of coping (e.g. culturally appropriate relaxation methods, accessing helpful cultural and spiritual supports);
- Encouraging, but not forcing, company from one or more family member or friends;
- As appropriate, offering the possibility to return for further support;
- As appropriate, referring to locally available support mechanisms or to trained clinicians." (IASC, 2007, pp. 118-119).

PFA TRAINING CURRICULA

While the World Health Organization (2003) and the National Institute of Mental Health (2002) recognize the importance and recommend the practice of psychological first aid, there currently exist few practical guidelines on how it may be implemented. A clinically useful set of guidelines for PFA is that provided by the National Child Traumatic Stress Network and National Center for PTSD (2005). This document defined PFA as follows:

"Psychological First Aid is an evidence-informed modular approach for assisting children, adolescents, adults, and families in the immediate aftermath of disaster and terrorism. Psychological First Aid is designed to reduce the initial distress caused by traumatic events, and to foster short- and long-term adaptive functioning. Principles and techniques of Psychological First Aid meet four basic standards. They are: (1) consistent with research evidence on risk and resilience following trauma; (2) applicable and practical in field settings; (3) appropriate to developmental level across the lifespan; and (4) culturally informed and adaptable" (National Child Traumatic Stress Network and National Center for PTSD, 2005, p.4).

These initial published guidelines stated that PFA was to be practiced by "mental health specialists," however.

Within the context of this volume, we define psychological first aid (PFA) as *"a supportive and compassionate presence designed to reduce acute psychological distress and/or facilitate continued support, if necessary"* (Everly & Flynn, 2006). PFA may be used in a wide variety of circumstances including the stressors of daily life, in family problems, in medical emergencies, in cases of loss and grief, and even in mass disasters.

At the Johns Hopkins' Center for Public Health Preparedness (CPHP), the following set of guidelines for the practice of psychological first aid were developed. The model is referred to as the RAPID PFA model and is summarized in Tables 10.1 and 10.2. The RAPID PFA model was developed specifically for utilization by individuals with little or no formal mental health training to assist both primary and secondary survivors.

Table 10.1
The Johns Hopkins' Model of
Psychological First Aid (PFA):
RAPID PFA - Overview

1. Reflective listening
2. Assessment of needs – start with basics
3. Prioritize attending to severe vs. mild reactions
4. Intervention
5. Disposition: assist to recover function OR facilitate access for continued care

---

The RAPID PFA model, then, is designed to be taught to public health personnel as well as emergency services and disaster response personnel (educators, administrators, and first line supervisors could also be trained in PFA). These individuals can then be the functional platform for surveillance, stabilization, and triage. More formal mental health services would be applied subsequent to the PFA as part of the overall continuum of care. Such a framework will also serve to allow mental health clinicians to attend to those requiring more advanced clinical intervention.

Table 10.2
The Johns Hopkins' Model of
Psychological First Aid (PFA):RAPID PFA

1. Reflective Listening
   • Event
   • Reactions
   • Paraphrase Content, Checking For Accuracy
   • Reflect Emotions
2. Assessment Of Need (Maslow's hierarchy)
   • Medical
   • Physical
   • Safety
   •Ability To Function
3. Prioritize – Triage Benign Vs. Malignant Reactions
4. Intervention – Cognitive-behavioral
   • Education: Explanatory (Use "Fight – Flight") And
     Or Anticipatory Guidance
   • Acute Cognitive/ Behavioral Refocusing/ Re-orienting
   • Deep Breathing/ Relaxation
   • Cognitive Reframing
     • Correction of Errors In Fact
     • Disputing Illogical Thinking
     • Challenging Catastrophic Thinking
     • Finding Something Positive, Hidden Benefit
   • Instillation Of A Future Orientation... Hope
   • Delay Making Any Life–altering Decisions/ Changes
   • *Caution! Do* Not Interfere With Natural Recovery
     Processes
5. Disposition: Assess That Person Can Adequately
   Function, Or Serve As Advocate/ Liaison For Further
   Support: Friends, Family, Community Or Workplace
   Resources
   • Identify Relevant Resources
   • Make Initial Contacts, As Appropriate
   • Follow-up, as indicated

The elements of RAPID PFA contained in Tables 10.1 and 10.2 are based upon eight core competencies, the abilities to (Parker, Everly, Barnett, & Links, 2006)…

- Demonstrate active listening skills,
- Prioritize and respond to basic human needs,
- Recognize and provide information on mild psychological/ behavioral reactions,
- Recognize and provide information on potentially incapacitating psychological/ behavioral reactions,
- Teach acute stress management techniques,
- Recognize and reduce risk factors for adverse outcome associated with intervention,
- Recognize how and when to utilize informal and formal resources for interpersonal support, as well as how and when to refer for more formal mental health care, and
- List techniques that constitute effective self-care.

SAFER-R:
A MODEL FOR INDIVIDUAL CRISIS INTERVENTION

The final model introduced herein is the SAFER-Revised model. The SAFER-Revised (Everly & Mitchell, 1999) model represents a protocol for conducting individual crisis response interventions (often referred to in the vernacular as "one-on-ones"). As such, it may be a useful psychological roadmap to follow as one assists an individual in crisis. **The SAFER-R may be thought of as an elaborated model of PFA**. By that we mean that it contains all of the basic components of PFA, but has the potential to expand beyond them.

- **Uses**: The SAFER-R model is designed for use with individuals in crisis. The SAFER-R model may be used on-scene during an acute crisis or disaster situation, or anywhere and at anytime after the initial impact.

- **Goals**: The goals of the SAFER-R model are those of most acute crisis response protocols, i.e., to mitigate the acute distress of the individual in crisis and to facilitate access to follow-up mental health assessment and treatment, if needed.
- **Format**: The SAFER-R model follows a specific progression of stages. The stages of the model are as follows.

Stabilization of the Situation

In this initial step in the SAFER protocol, the crisis interventionist assesses the impact that the immediate environment is having on the person in crisis and acts to remove the person from any provocative stressors (people or things) that may be sustaining the crisis and attend to any basic lower order Maslovian needs (e.g., food, water, shelter, clothing, safety, etc). This can be achieved by first introducing oneself and asking what assistance might be provided.

> "This seems really hard, how can I help?"
> "What can I do for now that might be of some assistance?"
> "What do you need right now?"
> "You look like you're having a hard time, how can I be of assistance?"

Things like "taking a walk," "getting a cup of coffee," or any other diversionary process that provides the individual with some "psychological distance" from the source of the acute crisis or any other situation may be of assistance. Prior to any such intervention, however, the crisis interventionist must always introduce him/herself and the role that is being served or performed.

Acknowledgment of the Crisis

The second step in the SAFER intervention is the acknowledgment of the crisis itself. This stage is fostered by a skillful use of basic helping communication techniques. In this stage, the crisis interventionist asks the person in crisis to describe "what happened" to create the crisis situation. The specific wording will of course depend upon the response in the previous stage.

"Can you tell me what happened?"

"What can you tell me about what happened?"

As a crisis is often punctuated by escalating emotions, this question gives the person in a crisis a cue and reason to return to the cognitive (thinking) domain, at least temporarily. Yet it is not usually advised to discourage cathartic ventilation unless the emotions are escalating out of control. Therefore, after having described the nature of the crisis situation, the person in crisis is asked to describe his/her current state of psychological functioning. A simple prompt such as, "How are you doing now?" allows the person who is in crisis to return to cathartic ventilation, but now in a somewhat more structured and secure manner. Thus, we see within this stage, the crisis interventionist has superimposed cognitive-oriented communications over the potentially labile emotional foundation. Later, however, having listened to the nature of the crisis, the interventionist encourages emotional ventilation in a safer, more structured communication environment.

Facilitation of Understanding

The third stage in the present model involves a transition back to the cognitive psychological domain for the person in crisis. In this third stage, the crisis interventionist begins to actively respond to the information revealed by the person in crisis during the previous stage. Here the person in crisis is encouraged to view his/her reactions to the crisis as generally "normal" (if indeed that is the case), expected reactions being experienced by a "normal" individual in response to an abnormally challenging situation (i.e., a crisis situation). The primary goals of this stage of the SAFER-R model are

- to assist the person in crisis in returning to the cognitive domain of psychological processing, and

- to encourage the person in crisis to see his/her symptoms as basically "normal" reactions to an extraordinarily stressful event, thus dispelling the myth of unique vulnerability or weakness. This, of course, assumes that the symptoms presented are "normal" and non-malignant in nature. If the symptoms are of a malignant nature, however, an appropriate explanation of that is provided as well.

Encourage Adaptive Coping

The fourth stage of the model represents what is usually the most overtly active stage with regard to the behavior of the crisis interventionist. Here the interventionist employs various "active ingredients" as a means of facilitating enhanced coping on the part of the person in crisis.

It is within this fourth stage that the interventionist will consider facilitating

- various "self-curing" abilities of individuals in crisis (e.g., further understanding, cognitive reframing, and self-efficacy); and
- active psychological or behavioral interventions (e.g., ventilation, problem-solving/conflict resolution, cognitive restructuring/re-evaluation, and other stress management tactics).

Because individuals in crisis are often plagued by what we shall call the "crisis triad," this phase of the SAFER-R model is directed most importantly at addressing those needs. The reader will recall that the "crisis triad" consists of

- tendencies for behavioral impulsivity;
- diminished cognitive capabilities (insight, recall, problem-solving), but most importantly a diminished ability to understand the consequences of one's actions; and,

- an acute loss of future orientation, or a feeling of helplessness.

The most direct interventions to address these concerns would be the "crisis intervention triad," as detailed below.

- Slowing down the interaction (assuming medical stability and no other objective urgency); suggesting a delay in any actions which have lasting consequences.
- Using the crisis communication techniques of summary and extrapolation paraphrasing to assist individuals in gaining insight into the consequences of actions.
- Providing a supportive, optimistic presence that conveys both directly and indirectly a future orientation; facilitation of access to continued care, if indicated.

Restoration of Adaptive, Independent Functioning or Referral

The goal of the previous four stages is always to assist the person in reestablishing adaptive, independent psychological and behavioral functioning. In the vast majority of cases, this will have been achieved by this point in the process. In some instances, however, it will be evident that the person in crisis is remaining in a highly unstable condition. If such is the case, the crisis interventionist's goal becomes that of providing assistance in obtaining continued acute care. Resources for such continued care might be family members, the clergy, organizational resources, or in extreme cases where no other resources seem suitable, an emergency room, or even law enforcement authorities.

SUMMARY

"[A] acute distress following exposure to traumatic stressors is best managed following the principles of psychological first aid. This entails basic, non-intrusive pragmatic care with a focus on listening but not forcing talk; assessing needs and ensuring that basic needs are met; encouraging but not forcing company from significant others; and protecting from further harm. This type of aid can be taught quickly to both volunteers and professionals" (Sphere Project, 2004, p. 293).

From both the acute clinical and public health preparedness perspectives, acute psychological first aid represents a potentially valuable skill set that is easily applied not only in the wake of disasters but also on a daily basis responding to the crises of everyday living. Arguably, wherever there is a need for the application of physical first aid, there can be a need for the application of psychological first aid. From a public health perspective, as we face threats such as pandemic influenza, terrorist attacks, and natural mass disasters, the need to respond to the psychological needs of primary victims becomes essential. As psychological status appears to predict behavioral response, addressing psychological needs may not only serve to reduce distress, but also may serve to improve compliance to governmental directives regarding personal and public health practices. It is unlikely that there will be sufficient mental health resources available to meet these public health needs. Therefore, it would seem important, consonant with the aforementioned recommendations, to train not only mental health clinicians, but non-mental health personnel as well, i.e., to train those outside of the mental health fields to provide some form of psychological first aid in order to meet psychological and behavioral challenges. (Everly & Flynn, 2006; Parker, Everly, Barnett, & Links, 2006).

CHAPTER ELEVEN

Pastoral Crisis Intervention

The pastoral community represents a large and often untapped resource in times of crisis. It possesses a unique aggregation of characteristics that makes it uniquely valuable amidst the turmoil of a psychological crisis. In critical incidents such as terrorism, mass disasters, violence, the loss of loved ones, and any events wherein human actions result in injury, destruction, and/or death, the pastoral community may possess especially powerful restorative attributes. Unfortunately, heretofore, there has existed no generally recognized and accepted manner in which the healing factors inherent in pastoral care have been functionally integrated with the well-formulated principles of crisis intervention. This chapter represents an initial effort to elucidate how the principles of pastoral care may be functionally integrated with those of crisis intervention. The amalgam shall hereafter be referred to as "*pastoral crisis intervention*" and is defined herein (Everly, 2000b; 2007).

PASTORAL INTERVENTION

As defined herein, pastoral care may be seen as the function of providing a spiritual, religious, or faith oriented leadership. Pastoral care is typically provided by someone (often ordained, but not always) who has been commissioned or otherwise selected by a faith-oriented group or other organization, to provide interpersonal support, assistance in religious education, worship, sacraments, community organization, ethical/religious decision-making, and related activities of spiritual support. From a more formal perspective, pastoral care is commonly provided by congregation-based clergy (and sometimes formally trained laity), chaplains, pastoral counselors, and clinical pastoral educators, while recognizing that these terms and functions are not mutually exclusive.

The opportunity for pastoral care interventions was formalized in the military on July 29, 1775, by an act of the Continental Congress. At that time the Congress allowed for the creation of an organized military chaplaincy. The opportunity for pastoral care, of course, existed prior to that informally at any time a member of the "flock" would seek guidance or support from anyone held to be in a position of pastoral leadership.

PASTORAL CRISIS INTERVENTION

"Pastoral crisis intervention" (PCI) may be defined as the functional integration of the principles and practices of psychological crisis intervention and disaster mental health response with the principles and practices of pastoral care/ support (adapted from Everly, 2000b). By way of parallelism, as crisis intervention is to counseling and psychotherapy, so pastoral crisis intervention is to pastoral counseling and pastoral psychotherapy.

FUNCTIONAL ELEMENTS OF PCI

The logic of the PCI may seem compelling, but the real value of such a construct emerges in its translation to practice. Everly (2007) has not only provided a definition of PCI, but has delineated its functional elements. They are listed in Table 11.1.

Table 11.1

Pastoral Crisis Intervention: Functional Elements

- ASSESSMENT = The evaluation of mental, behavioral, and spiritual factors/ status

- PSYCHOLOGICAL INTERVENTION = The use of basic, generic psychological principles and mechanisms of action to mitigate distress (see Table 11.2)

- LIAISON / ADVOCACY INTERVENTION = Serving as an intermediary and/or advocate to assist survivors in receiving the assistance they require

- SPIRITUAL INTERVENTION = The use of pastoral interventions generically applicable across religions / faiths; including Spiritual first aid

- RELIGIOUS INTERVENTION = The use of pastoral interventions based upon specific religious doctrine / belief / scripture

The goals of pastoral crisis intervention, as defined herein, are fundamentally the same as those of non-pastoral crisis intervention, i.e., the reduction of human distress, whether or not the distress concerns a significant loss, a crisis of meaning, a crisis of faith, or some far more concrete and objective infringement upon adaptive psychological or behavioral functioning.

MECHANISMS OF ACTION

In the context of this book, the pastoral orientation to crisis intervention brings with it a "value added" over and above the traditional non-pastoral approach to crisis intervention. This corpus of "value added" ingredients appears to be unique to the pastoral perspective as it employs religious, spiritual, and theological resources in an effort to "shepherd" an individual from distress and dysfunction to restoration. As a result of these unique strengths, it seems clear that some form of pastoral crisis intervention option should be integrated within all critical incident stress management teams, community crisis response efforts (Community Emergency Response Teams, Community Emergency Response Networks), and disaster response systems. Table 11.2 describes active mechanisms in crisis intervention, and further enumerates mechanisms unique to PCI).

Table 11.2
Active Mechanisms of Crisis Intervention
(from Everly, 2000b)

Traditional Mechanisms:
Early intervention
Cathartic ventilation
Social support
Cognitive reinterpretation

Potential Mechanisms Unique to Pastoral Crisis Intervention:
Scriptural education, insight, reinterpretation
Individual and conjoint prayer
Belief in intercessory prayer
Unifying and explanatory worldviews
Ventilative confession
Faith-based social support systems
Rituals and Sacraments
Belief in Divine intervention/forgiveness
Belief in a life after death
Unique ethos of the pastoral crisis interventionist
Uniquely confidential/privileged communications

Note: Depending upon the faith, more or fewer of these mechanisms may be active.

The reader will note the considerable degree of "value added" by the addition of the potential mechanisms of pastoral crisis intervention. It is important, however, that the pastoral crisis interventionist view the effectiveness of the pastoral mechanisms as resting upon a foundation of effective communication skills and differential recognition of patterns of acute stress, as well as the consideration of the more traditional active ingredients of crisis intervention as enumerated in Table 11.2.

Table 11.3 lists potential indications for pastoral crisis intervention.

Table 11.3
Indications for the Utilization of the Pastoral Crisis Intervention

- Receptive Expectations, i.e., the expectation/desire on the part of the person(s) in crisis for prayer, scriptural guidance, provision of sacraments, rituals, etc.

- Receptive State of Mind, i.e., while not specifically "expecting" such interventions, the person(s) in crisis is "open," or psychologically receptive, to pastoral intervention. It is important that argumentation, or debate, be avoided in the acute crisis state. Such actions tend to make the interventionist part of the problem" not part of the "solution."

- Pastoral crisis intervention can, obviously, be employed with not only primary victims of crisis, but with family members, emergency response personnel, observers, etc., but the same guidelines listed above would be applicable.

A WORD OF CAUTION

Thus far, pastoral crisis intervention appears to represent considerable added utility when used at the appropriate time and place, with the appropriate individual(s). Pastoral crisis intervention obviously requires significant insight and skill to act in such a manner as to achieve a positive outcome. Even then, it is not without its risks. Furthermore, it may be possible to mitigate such risks.

- Undesired preaching – Perhaps one of the greatest concerns associated with any form of pastoral intervention is undesired preaching. In a crisis, individuals are uniquely vulnerable. Often this vulnerability manifests itself in heightened sensitivity. While preaching the gospel (of any given faith or religion) may have uniquely uplifting effects for those who are prepared to hear the message, unwanted preaching may engender anger, avoidance, resentment, any even shame. None of these reactions would be perceived of as helpful in an acute crisis.

- Attempts to "convert" – The attempt to convert the person in distress to a new religious or faith orientation must be resisted. Noting the aforementioned psychological vulnerability of the person in distress, more fundamental spiritual first aid interventions would seem indicated for those receptive to spiritual intervention, while more traditional psychological crisis intervention would seem more appropriate in cases where individuals are not receptive to a spiritual message.

- Theological debates – The whole notion of provoking or even entering into a debate or argument of any kind with a person in acute distress seems beyond helpful. Not only does the person in distress possess a tendency to be overly sensitive to provocative cues, they possess a diminished ability to "hear" that which the speaker intends. Psychological alignment and the avoidance of conflict would seem a far better course of action.

- Minimizing suffering as the "will of God" – Anything that is perceived as minimizing the significance of a loss or crisis, or anything that appears to minimize the *validity* of one's acute distress is likely to engender resentment. Sometimes the best strategy is to admit that we are unsure as to the "why" of tragic events, while at the same time validating one's right to experience the distress. The pastoral crisis interventionist then participates in what is sometimes a difficult process of "attending to" and bearing witness to the distress of the other through a process of active physical presence, active listening, and silence.

- Using guilt/shame as motivation for change – The use of such tactics is controversial even outside of the context of pastoral crisis intervention. The use of such tactics within a crisis situation seems completely contraindicated.

SUMMARY

Pastoral crisis intervention may be thought of as the functional integration of crisis intervention and pastoral support. In effect, the practice of pastoral crisis intervention largely represents the use of faith-based interventions refined and augmented through the use of an emergency mental health delivery context. The value of pastoral crisis intervention seems apparent in situations involving death, serious injury, mass disasters, cataclysmic events such as war, and especially terrorism.

This chapter has attempted to review and expand the definition of pastoral crisis intervention as originally proposed by Everly (2000b). As defined, pastoral crisis intervention represents a potentially powerful addition to traditional community crisis intervention services. It is the newest addition to the integrative crisis and disaster mental health response system. Pastoral crisis intervention, even the use of pastoral resources, in times of crisis and disaster is not universally accepted, however. Its application, as with any other tool on the integrative continuum, should be reserved to those people and situations where it is most likely to be well received.

CHAPTER TWELVE

A Disaster Spiritual Health Corps: Training the Faith Community to Respond to Terrorism and Catastrophe

O. Lee McCabe[1], Adrian Mosley[2], Howard S. Gwon[3], and
Michael J. Kaminsky[4]

Excerpted with permission from Pastoral Crisis Intervention, *2007, Chevron Publishing*

This chapter describes the efforts of a partnership between several academic health centers and numerous faith-based organizations to develop a training program in disaster mental health for spiritual caregivers. The training curriculum integrated psychological first aid (PFA) content into a culturally-relevant spiritual framework. Nine pilot training sessions were conducted with 500 members of faith communities throughout Baltimore city and suburbs. Preliminary evaluation data indicate that trainees perceived the program as having significantly enhanced their knowledge of a model of crisis intervention that might be termed, "psycho-spiritual first aid," and increased their confidence in working with victims of trauma. The program is seen as having laid the foundation for an innovative, portable model of specialized early-responder training that can enhance the traditional roles of spiritual communities in public health emergencies.

The Role of Faith Communities in Disasters

It is well established that psychological casualties greatly outnumber physical casualties following terrorist attacks and naturally occurring disasters (e.g., Bradfield, Wylie, & Echterling, 1989; Shalev

189

& Soloman, 1996; Asukai, 1999; North et al., 1999; Boscarino et al., 2002; Galea et al., 2002; Schlenger et al., 2002; Ursano et al., 2003; and IOM, 2003). Furthermore, there are distinct sub-populations within the general population of disaster victims that are more at risk than others for developing acute and chronic post-trauma problems; these include urban minorities of low socioeconomic status whose vulnerability is often accentuated by chronic medical problems, severe mental illness, and substance use conditions (Smith et al., 1990; Lima et al., 1991; IOM, 2003; Pole et al., 2005).

Historically, faith-based organizations (FBOs) have been responsive in the aftermath of community disasters by providing tangible material resources, such as food, clothing, shelter, equipment, supplies, etc., as well as human services, such as death notification, prayer leadership, and general fellowship (Smith, 1978; Bradfield, Wylie, and Echterling, 1989). However, FBOs rarely are incorporated into formal preparedness and response operations of government (Koenig, 2006), nor are they fully recognized for their potential to provide effective emotional support for people with personal problems, in general (Verhoff, Kuhlka, and Couvan, 1981), or with trauma-induced symptoms following terrorist attacks or natural disasters (Chinicci, 1985), in particular. The failure to officially recognize the spiritual community as a vital, indigenous resource for frontline psychological interventions for trauma, and to foster the important community attributes of disaster resilience, resilience, and recovery (Kaminsky, McCabe, Langlieb, & Everly (2007) is inconsistent with survey data documenting that clergy routinely devote 15% of their (50 hour) work week counseling members of their congregations (Weaver, 1995 quoted in Koenig, 2006) and that the psychiatric disorders impelling congregants to seek help from their pastors are as severe as those treated by mental health professionals (Larson et al., 1988).

The premise of the program to be described is that the faith community is an especially valuable resource that can fit logically into local, state, and federal emergency response systems. However, if such a role is to be actualized, a number of challenges must be successfully addressed. These include creating the necessary collaborations among key stakeholders to develop appropriate training opportunities to teach crisis intervention knowledge and skills to clergy; establishing a trainee database/registry of prospective responders; and developing government/community linkages for call-up and deployment.

The authors addressed the above challenges by a) creating a partnership between several academic health centers and local faith communities to develop a training curriculum integrating disaster mental health content - specifically, "psychological first aid" (PFA; Everly & Flynn, 2005; Everly & Parker, 2006) with the values, perspectives, and communication styles of selected spiritual communities; b) tailoring the curriculum to fit the religious (*Christian*) and cultural characteristics of poor, urban African-American and non-English speaking Latino residents; c) collecting data to demonstrate participants' post-training perception of increased self-efficacy as a provider of disaster ministry; and d) establishing the administrative scaffolding upon which to build a volunteer trainee database and deployment infrastructure.

A Funding Opportunity to Expand the Role of the Faith
Community in Disasters

The opportunity to pursue these initiatives came in the form of a grant program, administered by the Office of Preparedness and Response of the Maryland Department of Health and Mental Hygiene (MD-DHMH). The original source of funding was the Special Projects grant program for hospital preparedness, sponsored by the Health Resources and Services administration (HRSA) of the U.S. Department of Health and Human Services. The grant application was developed by the Johns Hopkins Department of Psychiatry and Behavioral Sciences on behalf of Johns Hopkins Hospital and other partnering organizations [see 'Partnership Entities...' next page].

The Progam

Program Assumptions and Tasks

The logic of the grant application was that FBOs are ideal venues to support self- and other-referred individuals seeking trauma-related services of the kind needed following human- or naturally-caused community crises, particularly when a network of clergy has been trained in crisis/disaster mental health principles and interventions. To confirm this premise, however, the authors had to address multiple program design and implementation challenges in the brief period of time intrinsic to the HRSA (annual) grant cycle. Representative of these tasks were activities related to: establishing and nurturing institution/community partnerships; articulating the mission and vision; identifying objectives; managing day-to-day operations; designing and developing the curriculum; scheduling and conducting training sessions; and evaluating the program. These tasks were successfully accomplished and are described below.

Partnership Entities and Roles

Implementation of the project required coordination among numerous partners inside and outside the Johns Hopkins Medical Institutions. The intra-Hopkins participants included:

- The Johns Hopkins Office of Behavioral Health Care (JH-OBHC): JH-OBHC, in the Department of Psychiatry and Behavioral Sciences of the Johns Hopkins University School of Medicine, prepared the grant application and provided oversight of the post-award project implementation. The lead author (OLM) is the director of JH-OBHC, and was the Principal Investigator (PI) of the project.
- The Johns Hopkins Hospital (JHH): JHH, the first teaching hospital in North America, is a 1000+-bed, urban-based hospital with a long-standing commitment to the residents of

East Baltimore, and was the formal recipient of the grant award. JHH sub-contracted the day-to-day management of the grant to JH-OBHC.

- The Johns Hopkins Office of Community Health (JH-OCH): JH-OCH was created in 1991 to facilitate the formation of community-academic partnerships to promote the health of citizens in the local community. The second author (AM) is the Administrator of JH-OCH and served the role of Project Coordinator.

- The Johns Hopkins Hospital Office of Pastoral Care (JH-OPC): The Acting Director of JH-OPC provided significant input to the "disaster ministry" component of the training curriculum.

- Office of Emergency Management (OEM), The Johns Hopkins Hospital: JH-OEM is responsible for all policies and procedures related to emergencies that might have a negative impact on hospital patients, staff, students, et al.

- Center for Public Health Preparedness, The Johns Hopkins Bloomberg School of Public Health (JH-CPHP): JH-CPHP is funded by a five-year grant from the Centers for Disease Control (CDC) and provides a diverse array of preparedness trainings in the mid-Atlantic region, with teaching formats customized to a variety of adult learning styles. Its role in the project was to provide general advice on project implementation, including valuable input on culturally-appropriate curriculum content.

The external community partners were:

- Archdiocese of Baltimore - Office of Hispanic Ministry: The Hispanic Ministry was established in 1963 to meet the health and psychosocial needs of Baltimore City's growing Latino population, often disenfranchised by language barriers, socio-economic hardship, and cultural differences. It's role in the project was to provide advice on all matters related to the local Hispanic population and clergy, and to provide assistance with the English-to-Spanish translation of the curriculum.

- Clergy United for Renewal in East Baltimore (CURE): CURE, an ecumenical organization of clergy established in 1987, has a long history of collaboration with Johns Hopkins Medical Institutions. Through its member churches and clergy, CURE has worked to bring culturally appropriate health messages to East Baltimore's African-American church congregations and neighborhoods. The role of CURE in the instant project was to assist with outreach (clergy recruitment) to the east Baltimore spiritual community and with curriculum development. It's co-founder/immediate past-president also functioned as a trainer.

- Institute for Mental Health Ministry, Inc: The Institute was established in 2001 and provides a full range of clinical services, within the framework of a bio-psycho-spiritual model, to those seeking spiritually sensitive and inclusive treatment. The founder and director of the Institute is a board-certified psychiatrist who is also an ordained minister. He contributed content to the curriculum and conducted training sessions.

- University of Maryland Department of Psychiatry and Behavioral Sciences (UM-DoP): UM-DoP is well-known for serving the behavioral health needs of Baltimore residents, especially those in the western neighborhoods of the Baltimore City. UM-DoP was responsible for outreach to FOBs in the western neighborhoods of Baltimore City (while Johns Hopkins was responsible for outreach to the east Baltimore community).

A note on the Partnership Philosophy - Beginning at the grant application stage, the authors emphasized the importance of creating a cohesive, enduring academic-faith alliance. To accomplish this goal, an explicit "partnership philosophy" was articulated that recognized the following principles:

- Participants function in distinct cultures, and thus need to be committed to developing an environment that is mutually supportive of other partner needs;
- The principles of trust, respect, communication, flexibility, and mutual benefit are critical to the success of the partnership; and
- Collaborators are committed to sharing resources, and to developing compatible goals, realistic plans, clear objectives, specified tasks, and shared credit among partners.

Boards, Committees, and Workgroups

The project was implemented through a Partnership Steering Committee, a Curriculum Development Committee, and a Community Advisory Board. The Steering Committee was comprised of one representative from each of the partnering entities and the PI who chaired the committee. The Steering Committee met monthly for the first two months and bi-monthly for the duration of the project; this group made key decisions regarding strategies and tactics for project implementation. The Curriculum Committee was composed of at least one representative from all partnering organizations; it met on a weekly basis, and its members designed all of the content of the PPT slide presentation and Resource ('Tool') Kit. The Steering Committee and the Curriculum Committee were empowered to charter ad hoc committees and workgroups, as needed. Members of the Advisory Board, all of whom were leaders in the faith community, were selected by the director of JH-OCH. The advisory board met on a monthly schedule, provided helpful input on operationalizing the "partnership philosophy," and accepted accountability for outreach to members of their respective congregations to assure the recruitment of prospective trainees.

Program Vision and Mission

Vision - The long-term vision for the program was for the state of Maryland to formally recognize specially-trained leaders and congregations in the faith community as a vital resource in its continuum of frontline disaster workforce responders.

Mission - The near-term mission was to begin enhancing the capacity of clergy and lay leaders to respond to members of their communities who might need support during and following disasters of varying types and scope. The mission was to be accomplished through a training program designed by the partners. The project was originally conceived to benefit residents of the Greater Baltimore area, especially disadvantaged minority populations in the eastern and western neighborhoods of Baltimore City whose limited resources make them particularly vulnerable to disasters and large-scale community crises.

Program Objectives and Timetable

Award recipients under HRSA's Special Projects grant program must spend or obligate all funds by August 30th of the same year the award is given. Typically, notices of award are provided each year in the month of February. The project objectives during that compressed implementation period were as follows:

- to develop a customized disaster preparedness [Microsoft Power Point (PPT)] curriculum with content that a) reflected the cultures of the clergy and the vulnerable populations with whom they work; b) possessed biological, psychological and spiritual components; c) functionally bridged the public health and clerical approaches to an all-hazards mental health emergency response; and d) was compatible with state of Maryland's scope-of-practice statutes and related regulations;
- to develop a disaster preparedness curriculum with

knowledge-application and skill-building exercises that would encourage active involvement in training and promote the acquisition of competencies that would transfer to real-life contexts and circumstances;

- to develop a disaster "tool kit" that provided for trainees a comprehensive collection of practical resources;
- to develop a training manual to promote high fidelity replication of the model;
- to complete the program with a minimum of 240 trained members of the faith community;
- to develop a database of contact information on trained faith leaders that would be the foundation for a Volunteer Disaster Spiritual Health Corp Registry; and
- to establish the foundation for a formal liaison entity between the FBOs and local and state disaster management agencies for the coordination and efficient deployment of clergy during and following public health crises.

The Training Curriculum: Format, Content, etc.

Format of Training Sessions - Training sessions were conducted using a professional CME/CEU format, ie, one-day in length (9:00 a.m. through 4:00 p.m.) with lunch and morning and afternoon refreshment breaks. Each session opened and closed with a prayer. Program evaluations were completed at the end of the day, following which a "commissioning" of participants was conducted and certificates of attendance distributed.

Trainers - All training sessions were conducted by teams composed of one mental health expert and one clergy member.

Content - The topics covered in the training, listed in the sequence in which they were presented, are as follows:

- Stress Reactions of Mind, Body and Spirit: a) Acute Stress; b) Chronic/Cumulative Stress and Burnout; c) PTSD;

- Psychological First Aid and Crisis Intervention: a) Incident Command System; b) Individual Psychological First Aid; c) Large Group & Congregational Psychological First Aid;
- Pastoral Care and Disaster Ministry: a) Fundamental Aspects of Disaster Ministry; b) Differentiating Traditional Pastoral Care and Disaster Pastoral Care; c) Responses: Pastoral and Prophetic;
- Self Care and Practical Resources for Spiritual Caregivers: a) Recognizing and Preventing Burnout in Oneself; b) Self-Help Strategies; c) Disaster Planning and Resources for Families: Yours and Theirs.

A note on curriculum customization - To personalize the effort and promote identification with curriculum content, the authors asked faith leaders to incorporate into the PPT slides their own selections of prayers, scriptural passages, religious images, church photographs, etc. Additionally, a Spanish language version of the PPT-slide program was created.

Evaluation

Interpretations of success in meeting the objectives of the program were derived from traditional *process data* (number of trainings, number of persons trained, etc.) and *outcome data* (trainee ratings via a structured evaluation form, administered immediately after each training session). The scope of evaluation items spanned perceptions of *overall program quality* and success of the program in meeting *specific learning objectives*. These variables were measured using a 5-point Likert scale. Additionally, there were structured opportunities for respondents to provide open-ended comments and recommendations about future training.

Process Evaluation

Trainers, Training Sessions, etc. - Collectively, a total of eight trainers were enlisted, viz, two doctoral-level psychologists with extensive disaster mental health experience and seven members of the clergy, including the aforementioned minister-psychiatrist. Five hundred members of the faith community were trained in a total of nine sessions.

One Spanish- language training was delivered to 73 priests and laity from the local Hispanic faith community. Training sessions were delivered in diverse venues, ranging from auditoria of academic medical centers to small community churches, where attendees were seated in pews and trainers presented from a location in front of the altar.

Curriculum Development - The partners worked effectively in developing the 200-slide training program and tool-kit, the latter distributed to participants the morning of each training.

Database/Volunteer Registry - Basic demographic/contact data were collected on all trainees and incorporated into an Excel database, with a view to having this information as foundation for the eventual volunteer registry.

Call-Up/Deployment Mechanism - The JH-OEM will serve as the coordinating mechanism between the state of Maryland and the faith community to facilitate call-up and deployment of volunteers. The development of memoranda-of-understanding will be critical to this process.

Outcome Evaluation

A summary of the findings on trainee perceptions of the quality of the program is provided in Table 12.1.

The data indicate that the majority of participants considered the training either *very good* or *excellent* in overall quality and in accomplishing its learning objectives. The evaluation variable receiving the lowest score (73.6), ie, "quality of trainers: clergy members" was due to a relatively poor grading of one trainer's performance on one training day. [The occasion for this training was an annual conference of clinical pastoral counselors, all of whom possessed graduate education degrees. The training was conducted by an urban-based Baptist minister, filling in at the last minute for another scheduled trainer.

Table 12.1
Percent of Participants Rating Program as "Very Good" or
"Excellent" in Its Effectiveness in Meeting Specific
and General Objectives

General Objectives of Program Quality and Usefulness	Percent
Program Content	85.4
Likely Usefulness in the Event of a Disaster or Large Scale Critical Incident	84.3
Quality of Presentations: Disaster Mental Health Experts	91.8
Quality of Presentations: Clergy Members	73.6
Overall Program	89.1
Specific Learning Objectives	
Understanding the Principles of Providing Individual Psychological First Aid	85.5
Understanding the Principles of Providing Group/ Congregational Psychological First Aid	81.5
Gaining Awareness of Key Features of Disaster Ministry	85.9
Understanding Essentials of Disaster Planning and Self-Care Strategies for the Spiritual Caregivers	89.6
Understanding the Principles of Providing Individual Psychological First Aid	85.5

Though well-meaning, the trainer periodically chastised attendees for what he viewed as the participants' unfamiliarity with parts of the Bible, and generally tended to embody the fire-and-brimstone style of teaching/preaching. *It is instructive that the same trainer received exemplary ratings following a later training session with his own congregation, underscoring the importance of 'fit' between trainer/trainee characteristics.*] The evaluation process ended with the question, *Have you acquired any important information that you see being of help to you in the future as a leader in the clergy community*? The percentage of participants responding "Yes" was 98.4.

Conclusions

The authors' experience with this project has led to certain conclusions, the sharing of which is intended to benefit others who might seek to pursue similar initiatives in their own communities.

Notwithstanding the oft-observed tensions between large, urban-based teaching hospitals and their adjacent communities, the project demonstrated that, despite their disparate cultures, representatives from academic and faith organizations can enter into mutually-gratifying collaborations – in this instance, to lay the foundation for a disaster spiritual health corps, the members of which have confidence in their ability to respond effectively to terrorist attacks, natural disasters, and other public health emergencies. Crucial to the success of these enterprises, it would seem, are leaders on each side of such partnerships who are fervent champions of and models for the collaboration.

Participants were enthusiastic in their expressions of interest in the information conveyed in the trainings. They were especially appreciative of the efforts to *integrate* the technical disaster mental health content with the spiritual; they routinely referred to the training opportunity as "a gift from God." Although the prospects of large scale catastrophes were experienced as somewhat abstract or remote by some trainees, most participants had little difficulty finding immediate relevance in the training, as they routinely related the crisis intervention content to their everyday pastoral ministries.

Obviously, logical next steps in program advancement include the development of training curricula for members of other religious faiths. Based on specific trainee responses to open-ended questions in the evaluation form, there is also a need to create opportunities for: a) more advanced training in PFA; b) specialized training in loss/grief/ bereavement support; c) development of concrete, practical, community disaster plans (and community empowerment, in general); and d) clarification of specific respondent roles under various disaster activation/deployment scenarios. [These initiatives are currently being pursued in a second MD-DHMH/HRSA grant].

Summing up, the above-described program would appear to be a practical and eminently portable model for actualizing the latent but typically unrealized potential for specialized disaster assistance, inherent in the already established relationship between vulnerable urban populations and faith leaders (and probably rural residents for whom access to health professionals, in general, and to disaster mental health experts, in particular, is limited). By implementing this model of training on a broader scale, the faith community could actualize its full potential of being an available, effective, and durable resource for victims of large-scale disasters, with benefits accruing both to individual recipients of direct psycho-spiritual services, and to managers of health care facilities who are struggling with the problem of how to cope with disaster-driven surges in service demand under various hazard scenarios, particularly when front-line clinical staffing may be significantly reduced.

Acknowledgments

The authors wish to express special thanks to:

– The Office of Preparedness and Response (Director, Al Romanosky, MD, PhD) of the Maryland Department of Health and Mental Hygiene for the support of this project by a Special Projects grant from the Bioterrorism Hospital Preparedness Program of the Health Resources and Services Administration's (HRSA);

— Drs. George S. Everly, Jr. and Jeffrey M. Lating for their assistance in developing substantive portions of the disaster mental health training curriculum; and

— All members of the academic-faith community partnership whose contributions of time, effort, and intellectual content have made this project a potentially promising model for widespread application to the societal problem of disaster-related human suffering.

(Author Footnotes)

[1]*Director, Behavioral Health Care and Associate Professor, Department of Psychiatry and Behavioral Sciences, The Johns Hopkins School of Medicine; Joint Appointment, Associate Professor, Department of Mental Health, The Johns Hopkins Bloomberg School of Public Health.*

[2]*Administrator, Office of Community Health, The Johns Hopkins Health System.*

[3]*Administrator, Office of Emergency Management, The Johns Hopkins Health System.*

[4]*Vice Chair and Associate Professor, Department of Psychiatry and Behavioral Sciences, The Johns Hopkins School of Medicine.*

CHAPTER THIRTEEN

A Global Perspective on Crisis Intervention and Disaster Mental Health

Crisis intervention is neither exclusively an American development nor is it solely based on the work of the twentieth century. In this chapter we will update the practice of disaster mental health from the global perspective.

INTRODUCTION

The early pioneering trauma theorists and practitioners, who laid the foundations of modern crisis intervention services, came from many countries and some of them actually wrote their benchmark works in the late 1800s. For example, Janet (1889; 1893; 1894) and Charcot (1890) were French. Oppenheim (1888; 1915) was German. Freud (1915) and his colleague and good friend, Breuer (Freud & Breuer, 1895), were Austrian. Stierlin (1909) came from Switzerland. Erichsen (1866) and Myers (1915; 1916; 1940) were English. Cannon (1914), Salmon (1919), Lindemann (1944), and Caplan (1961, 1964, 1969) were American.

The platform for the development of an integrated, systematic, and multi-component crisis intervention program for distressed emergency and military personnel, as well as workers from a wide range of organizations, businesses, and communities was well-established by the mid-1980s. Many programs specializing in crisis intervention grew from the work of the early pioneers and rapidly developed, especially in North America and Europe. One such program, as noted throughout this volume, is Critical Incident Stress Management (CISM; Everly & Mitchell, 1999). The term Critical Incident Stress Management, of course, is applied to the large umbrella program or strategy under which there are many separate techniques. Within three years of the first article describing the basic concepts and techniques of Critical Incident Stress Management (CISM), the program appeared in Norway, Canada, and Australia (Mitchell, 1983, 2007). Other nations soon followed. Today the CISM program is employed by 28 nations worldwide. More than 1,000 CISM teams serve their communities in the aftermath of traumatic events.

THE DANGER IN RAPID GROWTH

When a new psychosocial program grows rapidly, especially when it crosses national boundaries, it may suffer from some unexpected, deleterious side effects. Cultural issues, inadequate training, preconceived notions, language barriers, traditions, flawed research methodologies, and hidden agendas often form barriers to the proper dissemination and utilization of a psychosocial program. Misinformation and misunderstandings, in the face of these barriers, are common. When those factors are combined with the new concepts and the new terminology of the program, the potential for inaccuracies, misinterpretations, and misapplications of the techniques is substantially increased (Mitchell, 2003).

Such was the fate of one of the techniques within the Critical Incident Stress Management (CISM) program. The specific crisis intervention technique for small groups, known as Critical Incident Stress Debriefing (CISD) became the subject of enormous misinterpretation and misapplication in a few communities. The challenge facing the application of crisis and disaster response interventions is to maintain the clinical fidelity necessary to achieve effectiveness across settings. Standardization, within cultural constraints, becomes an imperative. An earlier chapter discussed the so-called "debriefing debate" and the way in which much of the debate was fueled by misunderstandings regarding how the protocols should be applied. The root of the misunderstandings was lexical as opposed to substantive.

THE ENTRY OF THE UNITED NATIONS INTO STAFF CRISIS INTERVENTION

In 2004, the Director of Staff Counseling for the New York Headquarters of the United Nations created a crisis response team called the "Staff Outreach Support" (SOS) team. The peer support team received training in a wide variety of interventions. The value of the peer support program was demonstrated less than a month after the group training when a security officer committed suicide on UN property. People who were supported by the SOS program spoke highly of the benefits of the program and the helpfulness of the SOS staff (Sembajwe, 2005).

Around the same time as the development of the SOS program at the UN headquarters in New York, the UN Department of Safety and Security began a worldwide exploration of community, organizational, and employee support programs.

In early 2006, the first meeting of the Consultative Working Group for Stress Management, United Nations Department of Safety and Security met for a week. The Consultative Working Group held a second meeting in New York in December 2006. A course outline and training schedule were established and the group hammered out the details of the course content (Lerner, 2007).

In February of 2007, the General Assembly of the United Nations accepted and endorsed the resultant "Critical Incident Stress Management Unit" (CISM-U). Having reviewed relevant research and field applications of crisis and disaster mental health initiatives, the UN views the CISM-U integrative, multi-component program as a "best practices" approach to staff support.

The UN Department of Safety and Security offered two 90-hour training programs in Crisis and Stress Management for UN staff in 2007. The pilot program occurred in Glen Cove, New York in March, 2007 (UN Department of Safety and Security, 2007a). The second course took place in Paris, France in June, 2007.

The UNDSS Crisis and Stress Management course, which has a strong emphasis on classroom exercises, is outlined below.

- Day 1   - History and current theories of trauma and crisis intervention.
- Days 2 - Communications during crisis
-   & 3 - Individual crisis intervention.
- Day 4 - Suicide prevention, intervention, and recovery programs
  - Managing challenging crisis situations
  - Preparing to deliver information during a crisis
- Day 5 - Large group crisis intervention processes
  - Crisis Management Briefings
- Day 6 - Strategic planning for crisis intervention
- Day 7 - Small group crisis intervention processes
- Day 8 - Trauma interventions for extreme reactions
  - Immediate interventions
  - Post-immediate interventions
  - Complications of trauma
  - Long term trauma therapies
  - Managing rumors and panic in disasters
- Day 9 – Public Health Crises
  - UN Staff welfare issues
  - Psychosocial aspects of death
  - Psychosocial aspects of emergencies
  - Strategic Framework for implementing CISMU
  - UN deployment in times of crisis

- Day 10 - Multicultural and diversity issues
             - How diversity, gender and religious issues affect
               psychosocial services
             - CISMU procedures

INNOVATION:
IMMEDIATE SMALL GROUP SUPPORT (ISGS)

In the quest to provide an international standardization of interventions, the UN made two significant changes within the multi-component CISM-U.

The UN decided to rename the small group crisis intervention referred to as "defusing" with a clear, descriptive title - "Immediate Small Group Support" (ISGS). The ISGS session is provided very soon after a critical incident, within a few hours. The concept of small group herein refers to a primary group whose members know each other and work together. They share a common history and relationship to one another. In most cases, a small group has been together for some time. Crisis intervention personnel aim the ISGS at the group or unit that was most involved in the traumatic event. The ISGS is not to be used with individuals. "Support," in the term Immediate Small Group Support, means to "prop up" or "sustain." It absolutely does not imply any form of psychotherapy.

There are three required conditions for providing the Immediate Small Group Support Service.

- Small, homogeneous group (shared history, time and relationships)
- Situation is complete or has moved beyond the most acute phases.
- All of the participants should have had approximately the same level of exposure to the traumatic event.

The defusing or ISGS process has three segments. The first is a brief **introduction** of the trained team members who are co-leading the short meeting. The introduction also contains a brief description of the ISGS process and guidelines for moving through the meeting. The second segment is a **brief discussion** or exploration of the event itself. This discussion is very broad in scope. It is not necessary to gain a detailed rendition of the event. All that is necessary is that the people involved in the event discuss some of the key elements of the experience, especially any that had a personal impact on them. The discussion is guided by questions from the trained team members. The third segment of the ISGS is the **practical information and guidance** provided by the team to the group.

The entire ISGS or defusing process usually lasts between 20 and 45 minutes, depending on the size of the small group and the intensity of the situation. The crisis team members should initiate follow-up contacts with individuals immediately after the meeting, providing follow-up services, other support processes, and referrals, if necessary, according to the needs of individuals or the group.

INNOVATION: POWERFUL EVENT GROUP SUPPORT (PEGS)

The second alteration made by the UN involved a decision to use and alternate term for the the CISD process. The term "Powerful Event Group Support" (PEGS) was selected. We will reiterate our definition of the alternative terminology originally presented in Chapter 5. As noted in the title, the only time it is used is in the aftermath of **a "powerful" or traumatic event**. The word **group** in the name of the process indicates that the intervention is for small, homogeneous groups. The PEGS process should never be used on individuals. Finally, the word **support** indicates that PEGS maintains or sustains a group. The process should not to be construed as a therapy process. An analogy holds true: In the field of construction, pegs are used to hold things together. In the realm of small group support, the PEGS help to hold a group together and to enhance unit cohesion. A PEGS meeting assists a small group or unit to return to its maximum performance.

The foundations of the PEGS process are found in the Critical Incident Stress Debriefing (CISD). The original CISD model on which the PEGS is based was developed by Jeffrey T. Mitchell, Ph.D. (Mitchell, 1983; Mitchell and Everly, 1997). The rationale and protocols for the CISD process have remained intact in the PEGS process. However, the labels for not only the name "Powerful Event Group Support", but also for the specific stages within the PEGS are clearly descriptive and more accurately portray what actually occurs during a PEGS process.

It is crucial to our understanding of the Powerful Event Group Support process to note that PEGS is a proper name and refers only to one specific model of group psychological support. PEGS has seven stages. It is a structured, small, homogeneous group discussion. A typical group size ranges between 3 and 20 people. Depending on circumstances, the PEGS group discussion usually occurs between 1 and 10 days after a traumatic event. Most CISM teams aim to provide a PEGS at 24 to 72 hours after the event. CISM teams may delay PEGS sessions in cases of disasters in which operations personnel are engaged in the work for many consecutive weeks. Work crews must be disengaged from a disaster and adequately rested before they are brought together for a group discussion like the CISD or PEGS. In fact, a PEGS session should only be provided if three key conditions are present:

- The participants are part of a primary, homogeneous group.
- The event is over, or well beyond its acute phases, and the group has completed it work.
- The group members have experienced about the same level of exposure to the traumatic event.

The PEGS process was designed to achieve several goals. In most cases it should mitigate acute symptoms, facilitate normal recovery processes, aid the crisis team in assessing the need for follow-up psychological services, and, if possible, provide a sense of post-crisis psychological closure (Mitchell & Everly, 2001). Depending on group size and the intensity of the critical incident, PEGS may run between 1 and 3 hours.

Providers of any psychological services should receive proper training. Likewise, only those crisis interventionists with appropriate CISM training should provide the PEGS. The rule of thumb for the number of support personnel to run a PEGS is that there should be one support person for every five participants in the small group. *A minimum crisis support team is two.* If there are twenty participants, then there should be four support personnel and *at least one of them should be a mental health professional.*

Although the original CISD process was developed for use with emergency and military personnel, the current CISD or PEGS process can be applied to virtually any homogeneous group that meets the criteria. PEGS has been applied successfully to small groups in businesses, schools, industrial settings, organizations, churches, and, of course, with the traditional small groups such as emergency personnel and the military.

Table 13.1 outlines and compares, side-by-side, the traditional terminology of the CISD process and the alternative terminology of the PEGS process.

The UN Rationale for Clarifications of the CISD Process

As was discussed earlier in this book, under the section heading, "The Early Years,"Mitchell (1983), unfortunately used the term Critical Incident Stress Debriefing (CISD) to refer to both the overarching crisis intervention approach and the "formal" group discussion of a traumatic event. Mitchell recognized that this dual use of the terms was the source of significant confusion. Within a few years, the dual

Critical Incident Stress Debriefing (CISD)	Powerful Event Group Support (PEGS)	Step Objectives
1. Introduction	1. Introduction	- Introduction of team - Purpose of PEGS - Ground rules for PEGS process
2. Fact	2. Brief Situation Review	- Group members given opportunity to discuss a brief "thumbnail" sketch of the incident. They provide to the crisis team and to each other a synopsis of what happened during the incident.
3. Thought	3. First Impressions	- Group members given the opportunity to discuss their first impressions of the event. They may describe first or most prominent thoughts or feelings. Any aspect of the situation that initially impressed theCISD/ PEGS participants is encouraged - This step may provide useful information about the cognitive style or priorities of the group members.
4. Reaction	4. Aspect of Event Causing Greatest Personal Impact	- The group members are asked if there is any aspect of the situation that caused the greatest personal (psychological, emotional, or stressful) impact on them as individuals that they are willing to share with the group. - This step in CISD/PEGS is most helpful in ascertaining the nature of any belief system (worldview) violations that may have been caused by the critical incident.
5. Symptoms	5. Signals of Distress	- Group members describe personal signals of distress they have encountered as a result of exposure to the critical incident. - This step aids the team in determining who in the group might need additional assistance.
6. Teaching	6. Stress Management Information & Recovery Guidelines	- Signals of distress are normalized and "demedicalized." - Group members are asked to describe anything positive about the experience or anything positive they may have learned about themselves or about other group members from the experience.

- Group members are asked to make suggestions about personal stress management techniques.
- PEGS team teaches crisis management and stress management principles.
- PEGS team answers questions.
- PEGS team suggests guidelines for recovering from the critical incident

7. Re-entry	7. Summary and Final Instructions	- Answer final questions - Actively move the group members toward a "psychological closure" and an ending of the session. -Summarization is especially helpful in this CISD/PEGS step. - Bring up any "silver linings," positive outcomes, or common themes that are apparent. - Discuss any lessons learned from the experience. - Give final instructions for recovering, psychological rebuilding and "moving on."

use of CISD was abandoned and the term "Critical Incident Stress Management" (CISM) was adopted to indicate the overarching crisis intervention process. From 1986 and onward, "CISD" referred only to the structured group process (Mitchell, 1986; Everly and Mitchell 2001).

Despite efforts to correct the terminology, much confusion continued to revolve around CISD. The small group process was frequently confused with numerous other forms of ill-defined "debriefing" or "psychological debriefing." There are, in fact, numerous variations of the "debriefing" process. For example, among many other "debriefings" there are the Historical Event Reconstruction Debriefing (HERD), the Group Psychological Debriefing (GPD) from the National Organization of Victims Assistance, the Critical Event Debriefing (CED), and Psychological Debriefing (PD) (Dyregrov, 2003). Much of the confusion surrounding the use of the word "debriefing" lies in the fact that in the USA, "debriefing" generally referred to group crisis intervention. In the United Kingdom, however, the term "debriefing" typically referred to individual (one-on-one) counseling with medical patients (Rose, Bisson & Wessely, 2002). From the United Nations' perspective, PEGS has evolved from the CISD process in an attempt to move past the confusion created by the words "debriefing," "CISD," or "Critical Incident Stress Debriefing." The term PEGS will be used throughout the remainder of this chapter.

Tactical Considerations in the Application of CISD or PEGS

To be effective as a group crisis intervention, PEGS must be utilized strategically and in accordance with a number of important considerations and guidelines. The first consideration is the correct target populations. PEGS is only used with homogeneous groups (Ursano et al, 2003). Homogeneous groups are often functional work groups (an engine company in a fire department, a military platoon, a class in a school, an office workgroup in a business, etc.). "Debriefing of non-homogeneous groups (e.g., greatly varied exposures) can actually increase exposure of individuals to the traumatic experiences through the storytelling of others" (Ursano, et al., p.336). Thus, lack of homogeneity may be a risk factor for adverse iatrogenesis.

Timing is very important in the use of the CISD or PEGS. A group intervention that comes too early, when personnel are still engaged in the incident or too close to the end of the experience, will most likely be rejected by the group members. On the other hand, waiting too long may cause undue suffering and a rejection of the PEGS small group intervention as "too little, too late."

Group size is an important element of group process. Smaller groups are typically shorter in duration and may achieve greater cohesion. Larger groups become a bit unwieldy and individual needs have less chance of being addressed.

Crisis team member training is a crucial issue in the PEGS process. If the team members are not properly trained, they may demonstrate their uncertainty to the group or make serious mistakes in the management of the group as well as the individual members of the group.

Finally, like CISD, the Powerful Event Group Support process is not a form of psychotherapy or a psychotherapy substitute. It is only a crisis intervention, support process. Furthermore, it is not standalone process. PEGS is only one component within an integrated response system and it was not designed to be used in functional isolation or as a standalone intervention.

As presented in Table 13.1, the PEGS process has seven segments.

- **Introduction** of the team and the guidelines for the PEGS process
- **Brief situation review**
- **First impressions**
- Aspects of the event that had the greatest **personal impact**
- **Signals of distress**
- **Stress Management Information and recovery guidelines**
- **Summary**

These terms and clarifications should assist personnel in their efforts to conduct small group support services for homogeneous groups after traumatic events. Without much effort, trained CISM team members can easily incorporate the revised terms into their routine work with traumatized, homogeneous groups.

[For clarification regarding the manner in which ISGS and PEGS work within the Critical Incident Stress Management system of core components, see Chapter 5, Table 5.1 and the discussion that follows.]

CONCLUSION

With the endorsement of the United Nations, crisis intervention services can now spread more easily to more than a hundred nations around the globe. The international scope of crisis and stress management can now benefit many people who previously lacked trained resources to assist them through tumultuous times.

CHAPTER FOURTEEN

The Crisis Response Team: General Guidelines for Team Development and Leadership

A final consideration in any text on crisis intervention and disaster mental health must be on the crisis response team as the functional unit of intervention operations. Guided by NIMS guidelines as noted in an earlier chapter, the crisis response team serves as the human resource platform for crisis intervention and disaster response services. In this chapter we shall provide a very brief overview of general considerations, keeping in mind that three other texts may serve as useful and more detailed references (Dyregrov, 2003; Mitchell & Everly, 2001; Robinson & Murdoch, 2003).

BASIC ORGANIZATIONAL CONSDIDERATIONS

STEP 1: Identify the need for the crisis response team. Based upon identified needs, a rationale for the team's existence should both pragmatically and rhetorically emerge. In other words, creators of any given initiative should be prepared to answer the question "Why should this team exist, i.e., what need does it serve?"

STEP 2: Clearly state the goals of the crisis response team. Goals should be clearly listed and as behaviorally operationalized as possible. These goals will serve as the criteria by which the success or failure of the team will be determined.

Clearly state the constituency to be served by the team, "Who will be served by the team and to what circumstances will the team respond?"

STEP 3: Delineate guidelines for team membership and the specific roles to be performed.
- Administrative structure
- Dispatching functions
- Response functions, listing mental health providers' roles vis-a-vis the use of paraprofessionals (if applicable)
- Clinical mental health oversight/supervision
- Team member selection criteria

STEP 4: Determine how the team will be legally constituted.

STEP 5: Determine how the team will be funded.

STEP 6: Obtain legal counsel to operationally define issues such as malpractice, standards of care, confidentiality, "good samaritan" practices, necessary liability insurance coverage, et cetera.

STEP 7: Determine what criteria and mechanisms will be used to activate the team. Determine what backup systems will be used in the case of a mass disaster or widespread communication failure.

STEP 8: Determine what specific crisis intervention techniques will be used by the team (For example,

specify the interventions within Table 5.1 that are
to be employed.)

STEP 9:   Determine what criteria and mechanisms will be
used to deactivate the team.

STEP 10:   Stipulate guidelines and procedures for follow-up
with team members after a crisis response.

STEP 11:   Make arrangements for ongoing "in-service"
training.

STEP 12:   Create a clear, practical operating manual that
contains policies and procedures and addresses all
of the aforementioned issues.

THOUGHTS ON THE USE OF "PEER SUPPORT"

Whether providing emergency mental health services or traditional
counseling, the rapid establishment of credibility and rapport represent
a significant challenge for the interventionist in the development of the
therapeutic relationship. The provision of "peer" psychological support
represents an intuitively compelling mechanism for meeting such a
challenge, especially when dealing with recipients who are unfamiliar
with, or are otherwise resistant to, mental health intervention. If
cautiously applied and generously supervised, the use of peer
psychological support may allow the provision of psychological support
services to those who might otherwise avoid such support.

There does not seem to be a general consensus on precisely when
the use of peer (paraprofessional) counselors is most effective.
Nevertheless, the following guidelines may be of value. It would be
appropriate to consider using supervised peer counseling as one aspect
within the overall mental health delivery system for those instances in
which the group that is targeted for mental health services...

- is uniquely educated, compared to the general population;
- possesses highly unique occupational training (e.g., medicine, nursing, law enforcement, fire suppression, commercial airline industry, military);
- is resistant to, or threatened by, the notion of mental health services;
- possesses some religious or cultural characteristic that would complicate the provision of traditional mental health services; and/ or
- believes it is not understood, or is misunderstood, by the general population outside of itself, and/ or the traditional mental health community.

Clearly, the use of peer counselors may be efficient if it expands the availability of competent mental health resources, even though they require professional oversight and ongoing supervision. But can such paraprofessional mental health resources be clinically effective? In their classic treatise on effective counseling and psychotherapy, Truax and Carkhuff (1967) provide compelling evidence that the presence of three psychotherapeutic ingredients, specifically: 1) accurate empathy, 2) nonpossessive warmth, and 3) genuineness, in and of themselves serve to support psychological well-being. They provide evidence that paraprofessionals can be taught to provide these ingredients. They conclude, "The current available evidence, then, suggests that these ingredients of accurate empathy, non-possessive warmth and therapist genuineness are "teachable;" and even nonprofessional persons lacking expert knowledge of psychopathology and personality dynamics can, under supervision, produce positive changes..." (p. 111). Similarly, Durlak (1979) has stated, "Evaluations of research involving paraprofessional therapists have been highly positive" (p.80). There is evidence that groups as diverse as college students, parents, and community volunteers can be effective in providing psychological support. In a statistical review using Glass's meta-analytic formula corrected by gamma function, Hattie, Sharpley, and Rogers (1984) reviewed 154 comparisons extracted from 39 investigations. They concluded, "There does appear to be substantial evidence that paraprofessionals should be considered as effective additions to the helping services…" (p. 534).

CRISIS LEADERSHIP

Mayor Rudy Giuliani has said "Leaders need to be optimists. Their vision is beyond the present." This is even more so in crisis situations. In this chapter, we shall use the following definition: "Crisis leadership may be thought of as the provision of leadership before, during, and/ or after a state of crisis." Crisis leadership can be applied to assist individuals, organizations, and even communities/nations.

We believe that there are five keys to crisis leadership.

- **Preparation**. As Louis Pasteur once noted, "Chance favors the prepared mind." But preparation also means studying history. In 1514, Nicolo Machiavelli wrote a now classic text entitled *The Prince. The Prince* was a treatise on leadership. More specifically, it appeared to be Machiavelli's attempt to teach Lorenzo de Medici the core principles of leadership so that he might someday act to unite Italy during a period of chaos and decay. *The Prince*, as a pedagogical text, was largely based upon the "lessons learned" of history. In fact Machiavelli himself believed that the effective leader ("prince") must embrace the study of history. As George Santayana said, "Those who cannot remember the past are condemned to repeat it."

- **Direct action taken when necessary**. This notion is perhaps best summarized in the words of John McCain, "We are taught to understand, correctly, that courage is not the absence of fear, but the capacity for action despite our fears."

- **Perseverance.** The study of leaders such as George

Washington and Abraham Lincoln are testaments to the power of perseverance. But it may be Winston Churchill who said it best, "But for everyone. . . this is the lesson: Never give in. Never give in. Never, never, never, never—in nothing, great or small, large or petty—never give in, except to convictions of honour and good sense. Never yield to force. Never yield to the apparently overwhelming might of the enemy." - Winston Churchill, October 29, 1941, Harrow School, England

- **Communication**. An essential element of empowering others while fostering cohesion and support will be effective communications. In the final analysis, crisis communications should be designed to provide five essential elements.
    - Information (and rumor deterrence)
    - Reassurance
    - Direction
    - Motivation
    - A sense of connectedness, support
- **Learning from mistakes**. Oprah Winfrey has noted, "What I know for sure is that behind every catastrophe, there are great lessons to be learned...[what] we as a country need to get is that as long as we play the "us and them" game, we don't evolve as people, as a nation, as a planet."

CONCLUSION

With those words in mind, we end this volume with the words of Sir Winston Churchill:

"Remember we shall never stop, never weary, and never give in. . . . Good night, then: sleep to gather strength for the morning. For the morning will come. Brightly will it shine on the brave and true, kindly upon all who suffer for the cause, glorious upon the tombs of heroes. Thus will shine the dawn."

REFERENCES

abcNEWS (October 25, 2001). *Fear, and doctor visits: Doctor confront patients' anthrax fears*. Retrieved September 2, 2004, from http://abcnews.go.com/sections/living/DailyNews/doctors_antrhrax011025.html

Al-Nasar, F., & Everly, G. S., Jr. (1999). Prevalence of posttraumatic stress disorder among Kuwaiti firefighters. *International Journal of Emergency Mental Health, 1*(2), 99-101.

American Psychiatric Association (1954). *Psychological first aid in community disasters*. Washington, DC: Author.

American Psychiatric Association (1980). *Diagnostic and statistical manual of mental disorders, Third ed.* Washington, DC: APA Press.

American Psychiatric Association (1994). *Diagnostic and statistical manual of mental disorders, Fourth ed.* Washington, DC: APA Press.

American Red Cross (2001). *The ripple effect*. Alexandria, VA: Author.

Arendt, M. & Elklit, A. (2001). Effectiveness of psychological debriefing. *Acta Psychiatrica Scandinavica, 104*, 423-437.

Artiss, K. (1963). Human behavior under stress: From combat to social psychiatry. *Military Medicine, 128*, 1011-1015.

Asukai, N. (1999). *Mental health efforts following man-made toxic disasters: The Sarin attack and arsenic poisoning case*. Presented at the 11th Congress of World Association for Disaster and Emergency Medicine. Osaka, Japan.

Austin, P. C., Mamdani, M. M., Jaakkimainen, L., & Hux, J. E. (2002). Trends in drug prescriptions among elderly residents of Ontario in the weeks after September 11, 2001. *Journal of the American Medical Association, 288*(5), 575-577.

Bandura, A. (1997). *Self-efficacy: The exercise of control*. New York: W.H. Freeman.

Beaton, R., Murphy, S. & Corneil, W (1996, September). *Prevalence of posttraumatic stress disorder symptomatology in professional urban fire fight-*

ers in two countries. Paper presented to the International Congress of Occupational Health, Stockholm, Sweden.

Bettleheim, B. (1984). Afterward. In C. Vegh. *I Didn't Say Good-bye.* NY: E.P. Dutton.

Bisson, J.I., Brayne, M., Ochberg, F. & Everly, G.S., Jr. (2007). Early psychosocial intervention following traumatic events. *American Journal of Psychiatry, 164,* 1016-1019.

Bisson, J.I. & Deahl, M. (1994). Psychological debriefing and prevention of post-traumatic stress: More research is needed. *British Journal of Psychiatry, 165,* 717-720.

Bisson, J.I., Jenkins, P., Alexander, J. & Bannister, C. (1997). Randomized controlled trial of psychological debriefings for victims of acute burn trauma. *British Journal of Psychiatry, 171,* 78-81.

Bisson, J.I., McFarlane, A., & Rose, S. (1997). Psychological debriefing. In E. Foa, A. McFarlane, & M. Friedman (Eds.) *effective treatments for PTSD (pp.39-59).* NY: Guilford.

Blampied, N.M. (2000). Single-case research designs: A neglected alternative. *American Psychologist, 55,* 960.

Bohl, N. (1991). The effectiveness of brief psychological interventions in police officers after critical incidents. In J.T. Reese, J. Horn, and C. Dunning (Eds). *Critical incidents in policing, Revised.* Washington, DC: Department of Justice.

Bohl, N. (1995). Measuring the effectiveness of CISD. *Fire Engineering,* 125-126.

Bordow, S. & Porritt, D. (1979). An experimental evaluation of crisis intervention. *Social Science and Medicine, 13,* 251-256.

Boscarino, J.A., Galea, S., Ahern, J., Resnick, H., & Vlahov, D. (2002). Utilization of mental health services following the September 11th terrorist attacks in Manhattan, New York City. *International Journal of Emergency Mental Health, 4,* 143-155.

Boscarino, J.A., Adams, R.E., & Figley, C.R. (2005). A prospective cohort study of the effectiveness of employer-sponsored crisis interventions after a major disaster. *International Journal of Emergency Mental Health, 7,* 9-22.

Boscarino, J.A., Adams, R.E., Foa, E.B., & Landrigan, P.J. (2006). A propensity score analysis of brief worksite crisis interventions after the World Trade Center disaster: implications for intervention and research. *Medical Care, 44*(5):454-62.

Bowie, V. (1989) *Coping with violence: A guide for the human services.* Sydney, Australia: Karibuni Press.

Bowlby, J. (1969). *Attachment.* NY: Basic Books.

Bowler, R.M., Murai, K., & True, R.H. (2001). Update and long-term sequelae of the sarin attack in the Tokyo, Japan subway. *Chemical Health and Safety, 8*(1), 53-55.

Bradfield, C., Wylie, M.L., & Echterling, L.G. (1989). After the flood: The response of ministers to natural disaster. *Sociological Analysis, 49,* 397-407.

Breslau, N., Kessler, R.C., Chilcoat, H.D., Schulz, L.R., Davis, G.C., & Andreski, P. (1998). Trauma and post traumatic stress disorder in the community: The 1996 Detroit area survey of trauma. *Archives of General Psychiatry, 15,* 626-632.

British Psychological Society's Working Party (1990). *Psychological aspects of disaster.* Leicester, UK: British Psychological Society.

Brom, D., Kleber, R. & Hofman, M. (1993). Victims of traffic accidents: Incidence and prevention of post-traumatic stress disorder. *Journal of Clinical Psychology, 49,* 131-139.

Buckley, T.C., Blanchard, E. & Hickling, E. (1996). A prospective examination of delayed onset PTSD secondary to motor vehicle accidents. *Journal of Abnormal Psychology, 105,* 617-625.

Bunn, T. & Clarke, A. (1979). Crisis intervention. *British Journal of Medical Psychology, 52,* 191-195.

Bush, G.W. (2003). *Homeland Security Presidential Directive/HSPD-5.* Washington, DC: White House.

Busuttil, A. & Busuttil, W. (1995). Psychological debriefing. *British Journal of Psychiatry, 166,* 676-677.

Busuttil, W., Turnbull, G., Neal, L., Rollins, J., West, A., Blanch, N. & Herepath, R. (1995). Incorporating psychological debriefing techniques within a brief group therapy programme for the treatment of posttraumatic stress disorder. *British Journal of Psychiatry, 167,* 495-502.

Callahan, J. (1998). Crisis theory and crisis intervention in emergencies. In P. Klesspies (Ed.). *Emergencies in mental health practice* (pp. 22-40). NY: Guilford.

Campbell, D. & Stanley, J. (1963). *Experimental and quasi-experimental designs for research.* Chicago: Rand McNally.

Campfield, K. & Hills, A. (2001). Effect of timing of Critical Incident Stress Debriefing (CISD) on posttraumatic symptoms. *Journal of Traumatic Stress, 14,* 327-340.

Cannon, W.B. (1914).The interrelations of emotions as suggested by recent physiological researchers. *American Journal of Psychology, 25,* 256-282.

Cannon, W. (1932). *The wisdom of the body.* New York: Horton.

Caplan, G. (1961). *An approach to community mental health.* NY: Grune and Stratton.

Caplan, G. (1964). *Principles of preventive psychiatry.* NY: Basic Books.

Caplan, G. (1969). Opportunities for school psychologists in the primary prevention of mental health disorders in children, In A. Bindman and A. Spiegel (Eds.) *Perspectives in community mental health* (pp.420-436). Chicago: Aldine

Carlier, I.V., Lamberts, R.D., Van Uchelen, A.J., Gersons, B.P. (1998). Disaster related post-traumatic stress in police officers: A field study of the impact of debriefing. *Stress Medicine, 14,* 143-148.

Carr, C. (2002). *The lessons of terror.* New York: Random House.

Carville, J. & Begala, P. (2002). *Buck up, suck up…and come back when you foul up.* New York: Simon & Schuster.

Charcot, J.-M. (1890). *Lecons du Mardi a la Salpetriere. Policlinque 1887-1888.*Notes de cours. Tome I *et Lecons du Mardi a la Salpetriere. Policlinque 1888-1889.* Notes de cours. Tome II. Paris: Bureaux du Progres Medical, 2 vol.

Chemtob, C.M., Tomas, S. Law, W. & Cremniter, D. (1997). Post disaster psychological intervention: A field study of debriefing on psychological distress. *American Journal of Psychiatry, 154,* 415-417.

Chinnici, R. (1985). Pastoral care following a natural disaster. *Pastoral Psychology, 33 (4),* 245-54.

Conlon, L., Fahy, T.J., and Conroy, R. (1999). PTSD in ambulant RTA victims: A randomized controlled trial of debriefing. *Journal of Psychosomatic Research, 46*, 37-44.

Dalgeish, T., Joseph, S., Thrasher, S., Tranah, T., & Yule, W. (1996) Crisis support following the Herald of Free Enterprise disaster. *Journal of Traumatic Stress, 9*, 833-845.

Deahl, M. (2000). Psychological debriefing: Controversy and challenge. *Australian and New Zealand Journal of Psychiatry, 34*, 929-939.

Deahl, M.P., Gillham, A., Thomas, J., Searle, M. & Srinivason, L. (1994). Psychological sequelae following the Gulf War. *British Journal of Psychiatry, 165*, 60 - 65.

Deahl, M., Srinivasan, M., Jones, N., Thomas, J., Neblett, C., & Jolly, A. (2000). Preventing psychological trauma in soldiers. The role of operational stress training and psychological debriefing. *British Journal of Medical Psychology, 73*, 77-85.

Deahl, M., Srinivasan, M., Jones, N., Neblett, C., & Jolly, A. (2001). Evaluating psychological debriefing: Are we measuring the right outcomes? *Journal of Traumatic Stress, 14*, 527-528.

Decker, J. & Stubblebine, J (1972). Crisis intervention and prevention of psychiatric disability: A follow-up. *American Journal of Psychiatry, 129*, 725-729.

DeGaglia, J. (2006). Effect of small group crisis intervention (defusing) on negative affect and agreeableness to seeking mental health. *Brief Treatment and Crisis Intervention, 6,* 308-315.

Department of Veterans' Affairs, US Department of Defense (2004). *VA/DoD Guideline for the management of posttraumatic stress*. Washington, DC: Author.

Durlak, J.A. (2003). Comparative effectiveness of paraprofessional and professional helpers. *Psychological Bulletin, 86*, 80-92.

Dyregrov, A. (1997). The process of psychological debriefing. *Journal of Traumatic Stress, 10,* 589-604.

Dyregrov, A.(1998). Psychological debriefing: An effective method? *TRAUMATOLOGYe*, 4, (2), Article 1.

Dyregrov, A. (1999). Helpful and hurtful aspects of psychological debriefing groups. *International Journal of Emergency Mental Health, 3,* 175-182.

Dyregrov, A. (2003). *Psychological debriefing: A leader's guide for small group crisis intervention.* Ellicott City, MD: Chevron Publishing Corp.

Ehlers, A. & Clark, D.C. (2003). EArly psychological intervention for adult survivors of trauma: A review. *IBiological Psychiatry, 53,* 817-826.

Employee Assistance Professionals' Association (EAPA; 2002). *Report of the Disaster Preparedness Task Force.* Boston, November, 2002.

Erichson, J.E. (1866). *On railway and other injuries in the nervous system.* London: Walton and Maberly.

Everly, G.S., Jr. (1989). *A clinical guide to the treatment of the human stress response.* NY: Plenum.

Everly, G.S., Jr. (1993). Psychotraumatology: A two-factor formulation of post-traumatic stress. *Integrative Physiology and Behavioral Science, 28,* 270-278.

Everly, G.S., Jr. (1995). The role of the Critical Incident Stress Debriefing (CISD) process in disaster counseling. *Journal of Mental Health Counseling, 17,* 278-290.

Everly, G.S., Jr. (1999). Toward a model of psychological triage. *International Journal of Emergency Mental Health, 1,* 151-154.

Everly, G.S., Jr. (2000a). Crisis Management Briefings: Large group crisis intervention in response to terrorism, disasters, and violence. *International Journal of Emergency Mental Health, 2,* 53-58.

Everly, G.S., Jr. (2000b). Pastoral crisis intervention: Toward a definition. *International Journal of Emergency Mental Health, 2,* 69-71.

Everly, G.S., Jr. (2000c). The role of pastoral crisis intervention in terrorism, violence, and disasters. *International Journal of Emergency Mental Health, 2,* 139-142.

Everly, G.S., Jr. (2000d) Five Principles of Crisis Intervention: Reducing the risk of premature crisis intervention. *International Journal of Emergency Mental Health,* 2(1), 1-4.

Everly, G.S., Jr. (2003). Psychological counterterrorism. *International Journal of Emergency Mental Health, 5,* 57-59.

Everly, G.S., Jr. (2007). *Pastoral crisis intervention.* Ellicott City, MD: Chevron Publishing.

Everly, G.S., Jr., Beaton, R.D., Pfefferbaum, B., & Parker, C.L. (in press). Training for disaster response personnel: the development of proposed core competencies in disaster mental health. *Public Health Reports.*

Everly, G.S. & Boyle, S. (1999). Critical Incident Stress Debriefing (CISD): A meta-analysis. *International Journal of Emergency Mental Health, 1*(3), 165-168.

Everly, G.S., Jr., Boyle, S., & Lating, J. (1999). Effectiveness of psychological debriefing with vicarious trauma: A meta-analysis. *Stress Medicine, 15,* 229-233.

Everly, G.S., Jr., & Castellano, C. (2005). *Psychological counterterrorism and World War IV.* Ellicott City, MD: Chevron.

Everly, G.S., Jr., Flannery, R.B., Jr., & Mitchell, J. (2000). Critical incident stress management: A review of literature. *Aggression and Violent Behavior, 5,* 23-40.

Everly, G.S., Jr., & Flynn, B.W. (2005). Principles and practice of acute psychological first aid after disasters In G. S. Everly, Jr., & C. L. Parker (Eds.), *Mental health aspects of disaster: Public health preparedness and response,* Vol.1, (pp.68-76). Baltimore: Johns Hopkins Center for Public Health Preparedness.

Everly, G.S., Jr., & Flynn, B. (2006). Principles and practical procedures for acute psychological first aid training for personnel without mental health experience. *International Journal of Emergency Mental Health, 8,* 93-100.

Everly, G.S., Jr. & Langlieb, A. (2003). Evolving nature of disaster mental health. *International Journal of Emergency Mental Health, 5,* 113-119.

Everly, G.S., Jr. & Lating, J.M. (1995). *Psychotraumatology.* New York: Plenum.

Everly, G.S. Jr. & Lating, J. (2002) *A clinical guide to the treatment of the human stress response,* Second Edition. NY: Kluwer.

Everly, G.S. Jr. & Lating, J.T. (2004). *Personality guided therapy for posttraumatic stress.* Washington, DC: APA Press.

Everly, G.S., Jr. & Mitchell, J.T. (1999). *Critical Incident Stress Management (CISM): A new era and standard of care in crisis intervention.* Ellicott City, MD: Chevron.

Everly, G.S., Jr. & Mitchell, J.T. (2001). America under attack: The "10 Commandments" of responding to mass terrorist attacks. *International Journal of Emergency Mental Health, 3,* 133 - 135.

Everly, G.S., Jr., Sherman, M.F., Stapleton, A., Barnett, D.J., Hiremath, G., & Links, J. (2006). Workplace crisis intervention: A systematic review of effect sizes. *Journal of Workplace Behavioral Health, 21*, 153-170.

FEMA, Emergency Management Institute (2004). *National Incident Management System (NIMS), An Introduction IS-700 Facilitator Guide.* Emmitsburg, MD: United States Department of Homeland Security, Federal Emergency Management Agency.

Flannery, R.B., Jr. (1990). Social Support and psychological trauma: A methodological review. *Journal of Traumatic Stress, 3*, 593-612.

Flannery, R.B., Jr. (1998). *The Assaulted Staff Action Program.* Ellicott City, MD: Chevron.

Flannery, R.B., Jr. (2001). Assaulted Staff Action Program (ASAP): Ten years of empirical support for Critical Incident Stress Management (CISM). *International Journal of Emergency Mental Health, 3*, 5-10.

Flannery, R.B., Jr., Anderson, E., Marks, L., Uzoma, L.L. (2000). Assaulted Staff Action Program and declines in rates of assault: Mixed replicated findings. *Psychiatric Quarterly, 71*, 165-175.

Flannery, R.B., Jr. & Everly, G.S., Jr. (2004). Critical incident stress management: An updated review. *Aggression and Violent Behavior, 6*, 319-329.

Flannery, R.B., Jr., Hanson, M., Penk, W. (1994). Risk factors for psychiatric inpatient assaults on staff. *The Journal of Mental Health Administration, 21*, 24-31.

Flannery, R.B., Jr., Hanson, M., Penk, W., Goldfinger, S., Pastva, G.J., & Navon, M.A. (1998). Replicated declines in assault rates after implementation of the Assaulted Staff Action Program. *Psychiatric Services, 49*, 241-243.

Flannery, R.B., Jr., Hanson, M., Penk, W., Flannery, G. & Gallagher, C. (1995).

Flannery, R.B., Jr., Penk, W., & Corrigan, M. (1999). The Assaulted Staff Action Program (ASAP) and declines in the prevalence of assaults: A community-based replication. *International Journal of Emergency Mental Health, 1*, 19-22.

Flannery, R.B., Jr., Rego, S., Farley, E., & Walker, A. (in press). Characteristics of staff victims of psychiatric patient assaults: Fifteen year analysis of the Assaulted Staff Action Program (ASAP). *Psychiatric Quarterly.*

Flynn, B. (2003). *Mental health all-hazards disaster planning guidance.* DHHS Pub. No. SMA 3829. Rockville, MD: Center for Mental Health Services, SAMHSA.

Ford, J.D., Ruzek, J, & Niles, B. (1996). Identifying and treating VA medical care patients with undetected sequelae of psychological trauma and post-traumatic stress disorder. *NCP Clinical Quarterly, 6,* 77 - 82.

Frank, J.D. (1974). *Persuasion and healing.* Baltimore: Johns Hopkins University Press.

Freud, S. (1915). Thoughts for the Times on War and Death. Down loaded, 7/22/ 07 from http://www.panarchy.org/freud/war.1915.html

Freud, S. & Breuer, J. (1895). Studies on Hysteria (SE-2). *Standard edition of the complete works of Sigmund Freud, 24 volumes,* ed. by James Strachey et al. The Hogart Press and the Institute of Psychoanalysis, London 1953-74.

Friedman, M.J., Foa, E., & Charney, D. (2003). Toward evidenced-based early intervention for acutely traumatized adults and children. *Biological Psychiatry, 53,* 765-768.

Friedman, M.J., Hamblen, J., Foa, E., & Charney, D. (2004). Fighting the war on terrorism. *Psychiatry, 67,* 105-117.

Galea, S., Ahern, J., Resnick, H., Kilpatrick, D., Bucuvalas, M., Gold, J., & Vlahov, D.(2002). Psychological sequelae of the September 11 terrorist attacks in New York City. *New England Journal of Medicine, 346,* 982-987.

Gibson, M. (2006). *Order from chaos: Responding to traumatic events.* Bristol, UK: The Policy Press, University of Bristol.

Hattie, J.A., Sharpley, C., & Rogers, H.J. (1984). Comparative effectiveness of professional and paraprofessional helpers. *Psychological Bulletin, 95,* 534-541.

Hersen, M. & BArlow, D. (1976). *Single-case experimental designs.* Oxford, England: Pergamon.

Hobbs, M., Mayou, R., Harrison, B and Worlock, P. (1996). A randomized controlled trial of psychological debriefings of road traffic accidents. *British Medical Journal,* 313, 1438-1439.

Hoge, C., Castro, Adler, A., McGurk, D. et al. (2006). *Efficacy of post-deployment psychological debriefing with soldiers.* Paper presented to the 22nd annual Meeting of ISTSS, Hollywood, CA: Nov. 6.

Hokanson, M. (1997). *Evaluation of the effectiveness of the Critical Incident Stress Management Program for the Los Angeles County Fire Department*. Los Angeles: LACoFD.

Hytten, K. & Hasle, A. (1989). Fire-fighters: A study of stress and coping. *Acta Psychiatrica Scandinavica, Supp. 355, 80*, 50-55.

Inter Agency Standing Committee (IASC; 2007). *IASC - guidelines on mental health and psychosocial support in emergency settings.* Geneva: IASC.

Institute of Medicine (2003). *Preparing for the psychological consequences of terrorism:A public health strategy.* Washington, DC: The National Academy of Sciences.

International Federation of Red Cross and Red Crescent Societies (2003). *Community-based psychological support: A training manual.* Geneva, Switzerland: IFRC.

Jacobsen, L. & Vesti, P.(1992). *Torture survivors: A new group of patients* (2nd edition revised). Copenhagen, Denmark: Rehabilitation and Research Centre for Torture Victims in Copenhagen.

Janet, P. (1889).*L'Automatisme psychologique.* Paris: Alcan; Editions Odile Jacob, 1998.

Janet, P. (1893-1894). *L'Etat mental des hysterique.* Paris: Rueff, Vol.1 (1893), et vol.2 (1894); Marseille, Laffitte reprints, 1993.

Jenkins, S.R. (1996). Social support and debriefing efficacy among emergency medical workers after a mass shooting incident. *Journal of Social Behavior and Personality, 11*, 477 - 492.

Jonsson, U. (1995). *Slutrapport fran globen-projektet.* Stockholm: Polishogskolan.

Kagan, K. (1988). The meaning of personality predicates. *American Psychologist, 43*, 614-620.

Kaminsky, M.J., McCabe, O.L., Langlieb, A., Everly, G.S., Jr. (2005). Resistance, resilience, recovery: A new paradigm in disaster mental health services. In G.S. Everly, Jr. & C.L.Parker (eds) *Mental health aspects of disaster* (pp. 69-78). Baltimore: Johns Hopkins.

Kaminsky, M.J., McCabe, O.L., Langlieb, A., & Everly, GS, Jr. (2007). An evidence-informed model of human resistance, resilience, & recovery: The Johns Hopkins' outcomes-driven paradigm for disaster mental health services. *Brief Therapy and Crisis Intervention.*

Kardiner, A. & Spiegel, H. (1947). *War, stress, and neurotic illness*. NY: Hoeber.

Karsenty, E., Shemer, J., Alscech, I., Cojocaru, B., Moscovitz, M., Shapiro, Y., & Danon, Y.L. (1991). Medical aspects of the Iraqi missile attacks on Israel. *Israel Journal of Medical Sciences, 27,* 603-607.

Kennardy, J. (2000). The current status of psychological debriefing. *British Medical Journal, 321,* 1032-1033.

Kenardy, J.A., Webster, R.A., Lewin, T.J., Carr, V.J., Hazell, P.L., & Carter, G.L. (1996) Stress debriefing and patterns of recovery following a natural disaster. *Journal of Traumatic Stress, 9,* 37 - 49.

Kessler, R.C., Sonnega, A., Bromet, E., Hughes, M., & Nelson, C. (1995). Posttraumatic stress disorder in the National Comorbidity Survey. *Archives of General Psychiatry, 52,* 1048 -1060.

Kirwan, S. (1994) *Nursing stress pilot project*. Winnipeg: Manitoba Provincial Medical Services.

Koenig, A. (2004). *Content of exposure and health: Autonomic response to talking about a stressful event.* Thesis presented to Graduate School of Loyola College in Maryland.

Koenig, H.G. (2006). *In the wake of disaster: Religious responses to terrorism and catastrophe*. Philadelphia: Templeton Foundation Press.

Kobasa S.C., Maddi, S.R., & Kahn S. (1982). Hardiness and health : A prospective study. *Journal of Personality and Social Psychology, 42,* 168-177.

Konig, A., Lating, J., & Kirkhart, M. (2007). Content of exposure and death: Autonomic response to talking about a stressful event. *Brief Treatment and Crisis Intervention, 7,* 176-183.

Kraus, R.P. (1997). Randomised control trial of psychological debriefing for victims of acute burn trauma: Comment. *British Journal of Psychiatry, 171,* 583.

Krug, E.G., Kresnow, M., Peddicord, J., Dahlberg, L., Powell, K., Crosby, A. & Annest, J. (1998). Suicide after natural disasters. *New England Journal of Medicine, 338,* 373-378.

Krupnick, J.L. (2001). Interpersonal psychotherapy for PTSD following interpersonal trauma. *Directions in Clinical Psychology, 13,* 75-90.

Lakein, A. (1973). *How to get control of your time and your life*. NY: New American Library.

Langsley, D., Machotka, P., & Flomenhaft, K. (1971). Avoiding mental health admission: A follow-up. *American Journal of Psychiatry, 127,* 1391-1394,

Larson, D.B., Hohmann, L.G., Kessler, K.G., Meador, J.H., Boyd, J.H., & McSherry, E. (1988). The couch and the cloth: The need for linkage. *Hospital and Community Psychiatry, 39*(10), 1064-1069.

Lating, J.M., Sherman, M.F., Lowry, J.L., Everly, G.S., Jr., & Peragine, T.F. (2004).PTSD reactions and coping responses of East Coast and West Coast American Airlines flight attendants after September 11: A possible psychological contagion effect. *Journal of Nervous and Mental Disease, 192*(12), 876-879.

Lating, J.M., Sherman, M.F., & Peragine, T.F. (2006). PTSD reactions and coping responses of American Airlines flight attendants who were former employees of Trans World Airlines: Further support of a psychological contagion effect. *Brief Treatment and Crisis Intervention, 6,* 144-153.

Langsley, D., Machotka, P., & Flomenhaft, K. (1971). Avoiding mental health admission: A follow-up. *American Journal of Psychiatry, 127,* 1391-1394.

Lee, C., Slade, P. & Lygo, V (1996). The influence of psychological debriefing on emotional adaptation in women following early miscarriage. *British Journal of Psychiatry, 69,* 47-58.

Lerner, M. (2006). From the President's Desk: The Academy…Today. *Trauma Response,* XII, No. 1, p. 1-2.

Lerner, M. (2007). From the President's Desk: The American Academy. *Trauma Response,* XIII, No. 1., p. 1-2.

Lima, B.R., Pai, S., Santacruz, H., & Lozano, J. (1991). Psychiatric disorders among poor victims following a major disaster: Armero, Columbia. *Journal of Nervous and Mental Disease, 179,* 420-427.

Lindemann, E. (1944). Symptomatology and management of acute grief. *American Journal of Psychiatry, 101,* 141-148.

Lindy, J.D. (1985). The trauma membrane and other clinical concepts derived from psychotherapeutic work with survivors of natural disaster. *Psychiatric Annals, 15,* 153-160.

Litz, B., Gray, M., Bryant, R., & Adler, A. (2002). Early intervention for trauma: Current status and future directions. *Clinical Psychology Science and Practice, 9,* 112-134.

Lopez-Iblor, J.J. (2004). In Lopez-Ibor, J.J., Christodoulou, G., Maj, M, SArtorius, N. & Okasha, A. (eds.) *Disasters and mental health* (pp. 1-13). NY: Wiley.

Manzi, L.A. (1995). *Evaluation of the On Site Academy's Residential Program.* Research investigation submitted to Boston College.

Maslow, A. (1970). *Motivation and personality.* NY: Harper and Row.

Mayou, R.A., Ehlers, A. & Hobbs, M. (2000). Psychological debriefing for road traffic accident victims: Three-year follow up of a randomized controlled trial. *British Journal of Psychiatry, 176*, 589-593.

McCabe, O.L., Everly, G.S., Jr., Siegel, E., Heitt, M., & Kaminsky, M., (2004). Psychiatry and terrorism: The professional's role in disaster response planning. *International Journal of Emergency Mental Health, 6*, 197-204.

McClure, A.G. (1943). Effects of air raids on school children. *British Journal of Educational Psychology, 13,* 24 - 29.

McFarlane, A.C. (1988). The longitudinal course of posttraumatic morbidity. *Journal of Nervous and Mental Disease, 176,* 30 - 39.

Menninger, W.W. (2002). Workplace Violence. Paper presented at the FBI Critical Incident Analysis Group's Violence in the Workplace Symposium. Leesburg, VA.

Merriam-Webster's collegiate dictionary 10th ed. (1993) Springfield, MA: Merriam-Webster, Inc.

Millon, T., Grossman, S., Meagher, D., Millon, C. & Everly, G.S., Jr. (1999). *Personality guided therapy.* NY: Wiley.

Mitchell, C.S., Gochfeld, M., Shubert, J., Kipen, H., Moline, J., Langlieb, A., et al. (2007). Surveillance of workers responding under the National Response Plan. *Journal of Occupational and Environmental Medicine, 49,* 922-927.

Mitchell, J.T. (1983a) When disaster strikes ... The critical incident stress debriefing process. *Journal of Emergency Medical Services, 13* (11), 49 – 52.

Mitchell, J.T. (1983b). Guidelines for psychological debriefings. *Emergency Management course manual.* Emmitsburg,   MD: Federal Emergency Management Agency, Emergency Management Institute.

Mitchell, J.T. (1986). Critical Incident Stress Management. *Response*, September/October, 24-25.

Mitchell, J.T. (2003). Major misconceptions in crisis intervention. *International Journal of Emergency Mental Health, 5* (4), 185-197.

Mitchell, J.T. (2004). Characteristics of successful early intervention programs. *International Journal of Emergency Mental Health, 6* (4), 175-184.

Mitchell, J.T. (2007). *Group crisis support: Why it works, when and how to provide it.* Ellicott City, MD: Chevron Publishing.

Mitchell, J.T. & Everly, G.S., Jr. (1993). *Human elements training in Emergency Services.* Ellicott City, MD: Chevron Publishing Corporation.

Mitchell, J.T. & Everly, G.S., Jr. (1996). *Critical Incident Stress Debriefing: An operations manual for the prevention of traumatic stress among emergency services and disaster workers.* Ellicott City, MD: Chevron Publishing Corporation.

Mitchell, J.T. & Everly, G.S., Jr. (1997). Scientific evidence for Critical Incident Stress Management. *Journal of Emergency Medical Services, 22,* 87 - 93.

Mitchell, J.T. & Everly, G.S., Jr. (2001) *Critical Incident Stress Debriefing: An operations manual for CISD, defusing, and other group crisis intervention services (3rd ed.).* Ellicott City, MD: Chevron Publishing Corp

Mitchell, S.G. & Mitchell, J.T. (2006). Caplan, Community and Critical Incident Stress Management. *International Journal of Emergency Mental Health, 8*(1), 1-10.

Myers, C.S. (1915-1916). Contributions to the study of shell-shock (I)Being an account of three cases of loss of memory, vision, smell and taste, admitted into the Duchess of Westminister's war hospital, Le Touquet. *Lancet,* 13 fev. 1915, p.316-20. (II) Being an account of certain cases treated by hypnosis. *Lancet,* 8 janv. 1916, p. 65-69. (III) Being an account of certain disorder of cutaneous sensibility. *Lancet,* 18 mars 1916, p.608-613. (IV) Being an account of certain disorders of speech, with special reference to their causation and their relation with malingering, *Lancet,* 9 sept. 1916, p. 461-467.

Myers, C.S. (1940). *Shell-shock in France 1914-1918,* Cambridge; Cambridge University Press.

National Child Traumatic Stress Network and National Center for PTSD (2005, September). Psychological First Aid: Field operations guide. Washington, DC: Author. Retrieved from http://www.ncptsd.va.gov/pfa/PFA_9_6_05_Final.pdf.

National Incident Management System Integration Center (2007a). *NIMS Training.* Washington, DC: United States Department of Homeland Security, Federal Emergency Management Agency.

National Incident Management System Integration Center (2007b). *NIMS Guide.* Washington, DC: United States Department of Homeland Security, Federal Emergency Management Agency.

National Incident Management System Integration Center (2007c). *National Incident Management System (NIMS) – National Standard Curriculum Training Development Guidance – FY07.* Washington, DC: United States Department of Homeland Security, Federal Emergency Management Agency.

National Incident Management System Integration Center (2007d). *WELCOME to the National Incident Management System Integration Center.* Washington, DC: United States Department of Homeland Security, Federal Emergency Management Agency.

National Institute of Mental Health (2002). *Mental health and mass violence.* Washington, D.C.: Author.

NIMSonline.com (2004). NIMS- ICS Graphics. Washington, DC: NIMS on line.com

National Volunteer Organizations Active in Disaster, Early Psychological Intervention Subcommittee (2005, May). Early Psychological Intervention Consensus Points.

National Wildfire Coordinating Group (1994). A history of the Incident Command System. In NWCG *Incident Command System (ICS) national training curriculum.* Washington, DC: NIMS on line.com.

Neil, T.C., Oney, J.E., DiFonso, L., Thacker, B., & Reichart, W. (1974). *Emotional first aid.* Louisville, KY: Kemper-Behavioral Science Associates.

Newman. E.C. (2000). Group crisis intervention in a school setting following an attempted suicide. *International Journal of Emergency Mental Health, 2,* 97-100.

North, C.S., McCutcheon, V., Spitznagel, E.L., & Smith, E.S. (2002a). *Three-tear follow-up of survivors of a mass shooting episode.* Journal of Urban Health, 79, 383-391.

North, C.S., Nixon, S., Shariat, S., Malonee, S., McMillen, J.C., Spitznagel, K.P. & Smith, E. (1999). Psychiatric disorders among survivors of the Oklahoma City bombing. *Journal of the American Medical Association, 282,* 755-762.

North, C.S., Pfefferbaum, B., & Tucker, P. (2002b). Ethical and methodological issues in academic mental health research in populations affected by disasters. The Oklahoma City experience relevant to September 11, 2001. *CNS Spectrums, 7*, 580-584.

North, C.S., Smith, E., & Spitznagel, E. (1994). Posttraumatic stress disorder in survivors of a mass shooting. *American Journal of Psychiatry, 151*, 82-88.

North, C. S., Tivis, L., McMillen, J.C., Pfefferbaum, B., Cox, J., Spitznagel, E.L., Nixon, S., Bunch, K.P., Schorr, J. & Smith, E. (2002c). Coping, functioning, and adjustment of rescue workers after the Oklahoma City bombing. *Journal of Traumatic Stress, 15*, 171-175.

North, C.S., Tivis, L., McMillen, J.C., Pfefferbaum, B., Spitznagel, E.L., Cox, J., Nixon, S., Bunch, K.P. & Smith, E. (2002d). Psychiatric disorders in rescue workers after the Oklahoma City bombing. *American Journal of Psychiatry, 159*, 857-859.

Nurmi, L. (1999). The sinking of the Estonia: The effects of Critical Incident Stress Debriefing on Rescuers. *International Journal of Emergency Mental Health, 1*, 23-32.

Ohbu, S., Yamashina, A., Takasu, N., Yamaguchi, T., Murai, T., Nakano, K., Matsui, Y.,

Mikami, R., Sakurai, K., & Hinohara, S. (1997). Sarin poisoning on Tokyo subway. *Southern Medical Journal, 90*(6), 587-593.

Oppenheim, H. (1888). *Die traumatischen neurosen.* Berlin: V. Von August Hirshwald, ed., 1892 (2nd ed.).

Oppenheim, H. (1915). *Der krieg und die traumatische Neurose.* Berlin: Clik. Wochenschr., mars, 11, pp.257-261.

OSHA. (2001). *How to plan for workplace emergencies and evacuations.* Washington, DC: Author.

Parad, H. (1966). The use of time limited crisis intervention in community mental health programming. *Social Service Review, 40*, 275-282.

Parad, L. & Parad, H. (1968). A study of crisis oriented planned short-term treatment: Part II. *Social Casework, 49*, 418-426.

Parker, C.L., Barnett, D.J.., Everly, G.S., Jr., & Links, J.M. (2006). Expanding disaster mental health response: A conceptual training framework for public health personnel. *International Journal of Emergency Mental Health, 8*, 101-109.

Parker, C.L., Everly, G.S., Jr., Barnett, D.J.., & Links, J.M. (2006). Establishing evidence-informed core intervention competencies in psychological first aid for public health personnel. *International Journal of Emergency Mental Health, 8*, 83-92.

Paul, G. (1967). Strategy of outcome research in psychotherapy. *Journal of Consulting and Clinical Psychology, 31,* 109-118.

Paul, J. & Blum, D. (2005). Workplace Disaster Preparedness and response: the employee assistance program continuum of services. *International Journal of Emergency Mental Health, 7,* 169-178.

Pennebaker, J.W. (1985). Traumatic experience and psychosomatic disease. *Canadian Psychologist, 26*, 82-95.

Pennebaker, J.W. (1990). *Opening up: The healing power of confiding in others*. NY: Avon.

Pennebaker, J.W. (1999). The effects of traumatic exposure on physical and mental health: The values of writing and talking about upsetting events. *International Journal of Emergency Mental Health, 1*, 9-18.

Pennebaker, J.W. & Beall, S. (1986). Confronting a traumatic event. *Journal of Abnormal Psychology*, *95*, 274-281.

Pfefferbaum, B. & Pfefferbaum, R.L. (1998). Contagion in stress. *Child and Adolescent Psychiatric Clinics of North America, 1*, 183-194.

Pole, N., Best, S.R., Metzler, T., & Marmar, C.R. (2005). Why are Hispanics at greater risk for PTSD? *Cultural Diversity & Ethnic Minority Psychology, 11,* 144-161.

Post, R. (1992). Transduction of psychosocial stress onto the neurobiology of recurrent affective disorder. *American Journal of Psychiatry, 149,* 990-1010.

Professional Practice Board Working Party (2002). *Psychological debriefing*. Leicester, UK: British Psychological Society.

Raphael, B. (1986). *When disaster strikes*. NY: Basic Books.

Rapoport, L. (1965). The state of crisis. In H. Parad (Ed.). *Crisis intervention: Selected readings*. NY: Family Service Association of America.

Richards, D. (1999, April). *A field study of CISD v. CISM*. Paper presented to the Fifth World Congress on Stress, Trauma and Coping in the Emergency Services Professions, Baltimore.

Ritchie, E.C., Friedman, M., Watson, P., Ursano, R., Wessely, S., & Flynn, B. (2004). *Military Medicine, 169,* 575-579.

Roan, S. (October 27, 2001). Anthrax scare poses danger of mass illness hysteria. *The* Detroit News.

Roberts, A.R. (2005) Bridging the Past and Present to the Future of Crisis Intervention and Crisis Management. In A.R. Roberts (Ed.) *Crisis intervention handbook: Assessment, treatment, research.* New York: Oxford University Press.

Robinson, H., Sigman, M., & Wison, J. (1997). Duty-related stressors and PTSD symptoms in suburban police officers. *Psychological Reports, 81,* 835-845.

Robinson, R. (2003). Personal communication.

Robinson, R. (2007). Commentary on "Issues in the debriefing debate for emergency services." *Clinical Psychology: Science and Practice, 14,* 121-123.

Robinson, R.C. & Mitchell, J.T. (1993). Evaluation of psychological debriefings. *Journal of Traumatic Stress, 6*(3), 367-382.

Robinson, R.C. & Mitchell, J.T. (1995). Getting some balance back into the debriefing debate. *The Bulletin of the Australian Psychological Society, 17*(10), 5-10.

Robinson, R.C. & Murdoch, P. (2003). *Establishing and maintaining peer support programs in the workplace.* Ellicott City: MD: Chevron Publishing Corp.

Rogers, C. (1951). *Client-centered therapy.* Boston: Houghton Mifflin.

Rose, S., Berwin, C.R., Andrews, B. & Kirk, M. (1999). A randomized controlled trial of individual psychological debriefing for victims of violent crime. *Psychological Medicine*, 29, 793-799.

Rose, S., Bisson, J., & Wessely, S. (2002). Psychological debriefing for preventing post traumatic stress disorder (PTSD). *The Cochrane Library*, Issue 1. Oxford, UK: Update Software.

Rossi, P.H. & Freeman, H.E. (1985). *Evaluation: A systematic approadh.* Beverly Hills, CA: Sage.

Ruzek, J.I., Young, B.H., Cordova, M.J., Flynn, B.W. (2004). Integration of disaster mental health with emergency medicine. *Prehospital and Disaster Medicine, 19*(1), 46-53.

Salmon, T. (1919). War neuroses and their lesson. *New York Medical Journal, 108,* 993-994.

Sargant, W. (1942). Physical treatment of acute war neurosis. *British Medical Journal, Nov 14, 1942,* 574-576.

Schlenger, W.E., Caddell, J.M., Ebert, L., Jordan, K.B., Rourke, K.M., Wilson, D., Thalji, L., Dennis, J.M., Fairbank, J.A., & Kulka, R.A. (2002). Psychological reactions to terrorist attacks: Findings from the national study of Americans' reactions to September 11. *Journal of the American Medical Association, 288,* 581 - 588.

Seligman, M.E.P. (1995). The effectiveness of psychotherapy. *American Psychologist, vol. 29, (12),* 965-974.

Sembajwe, R. (2005). Personal Communication.

Shalev, A.Y., Peri, T., Rogel Fuchs, Y., Ursano, R.J., & Marlowe, D. (1998). Historical group debriefing after combat exposure. *Military Medicine, 163*(7), 494-498.

Shalev, A.Y., & Solomon, Z. (1996). The threat and fear of missile attack: Israelis in the Gulf War. In R.J. Ursano and A.E. Norwood (Eds.), *Emotional aftermath of the Persian Gulf War: Veterans, families, communities, and nations* (pp. 143-160). Washington, DC: American Psychiatric Press, Inc.

Sheehan, D., Everly, G.S., Jr., & Langlieb, A. (2004). *Current best practices coping with major critical incidents.* FBI Law Enforcement Bulletin, v. 73, #9, 1-13.

Slaby, A., Lieb, J., & Tancredi, L. (1975) *Handbook of psychiatric emergencies.* Flushing, NY: Medical Examination Publishing.

Slaikeu, K.A. (1990). *Crisis intervention.* Boston: Allyn and Bacon.

Small, R., Lumley, J., Donohue, L., Potter, A. & Waldenstrom, U. (2000). Randomized controlled trial of midwife led debriefing to reduce maternal depression after operative childbirth. *British Medical Journal, 321,* 1043-1047.

Smith, M.H. (1978). American religious organizations in disaster: A study of congregational response to disaster, *Mass Emergencies, 3,* 133-42.

Smith, E.M., North, C.S., McCool, R.E., & Shea, J.M. (1990). Acute post-disaster psychiatric disorders: Identification of persons at risk. *American Journal of Psychiatry, 147*(2), 202-206.

Solomon, Z. & Benbenishty, R. (1986). The role of proximity, immediacy, and expectancy in frontline treatment of combat stress reaction among Israelis in the Lebanon War. *American Journal of Psychiatry, 143,* 613-617.

Solomon, Z., Shklar, R. and Mikulincer, M. (2005). Frontline treatment of combat stress reaction: A 20-year longitudinal evaluation study, *American Journal of Psychiatry, 162,* 2309-2314.

Sphere Project (2004). *Sphere Project handbook, Revised.* Geneva: Author.

Spiegel, D. & Classen, C. (1995). Acute stress disorder. In   G. Gabbard (Ed.). *Treatments of psychiatric disorders* (pp.1521-1537). Washington, DC: American Psychiatric Press.

Stapleton, A., Lating, J.M., Kirkhart, M. & Everly, G.S., Jr. (2006). Effects of medical crisis intervention on anxiety, depression, and posttraumatic stress symptoms: A meta-analysis. *Psychiatric Quarterly, 77,* 231-238

Stierlin, E. (1909) *Psycho-neuropathology as a result of a mining disaster March 10, 1906.* Zurich: University of Zurich.

Taylor, S. (1983). Adjustment to threatening events. *American Psychologist, 38,* 1161-1173.

Tebes, J.K. (2000). External validity and scientific psychology. *American Psychologist, 55,* 1508-1509.

Thorne, F.C. (1952). Psychological first ais. *Journal of Clinical Psychology, 8*(2), 210-211.

Truax, C.B. & Carkhuff, R. (1967). *Toward effective counseling and psychotherapy.* Chicago: Aldine.

Tuckey, M.R. (2007). Issues in the debriefing debate for emergency services. *Child Psychology: Science and Practice, 14,* 106-116.

Turnbull, G., Busuttil, W., & Pittman, S. (1997). Psychological debriefing for victims of acute burn trauma. *British Journal of Psychiatry, 171,* 582.

United Nations Department of Safety and Security CISMU Staff (2007a). UNDSS CISMU Certification Training For Counsellors. *DSS Newsletter.* New York: United Nations Secretariat, Department of Safety and Security.

United Nations Department of Safety and Security CISMU Staff (2007b). New crisis and stress management training programme launched. *I Seek (May 2, 2007)* New York: United Nations Secretariat.

United Nations Department of Safety and Security CISMU Staff (2007c). *Certification training in Crisis and Stress Management.* New York: UN Department of Safety and Security, Consultative Working Group on Stress in

Collaboration with the International Critical Incident Stress Foundation, the American Academy of Experts in Traumatic Stress and the Comite National de L'urgence Medico-Psychologigue.

United States Coast Guard (2001). *Incident Management Handbook.* Washington, DC: United States Printing Office (COMDTPUB P3120.17).

United States Coast Guard (2006). *Incident Management Handbook.* Washington, DC: United States Printing Office (COMDTPUB P3120.17A).

United States Department of Homeland Security (2004). *National Incident Management System.* Washington, DC: United States Department of Homeland Security, Federal Emergency Management Agency.

Ursano, R., McCarroll, C., &Fullerton, C. (2003). Traumatic death in terrorism and disasters. In R. Ursano, C. Fullerton, & A. Norwood (Eds.) *Terrorism and disaster* (pp.333-339). Cambridge, UK : Cambridge University Press.

Ursano, R.J., Norwood, A.E., Fullerton, C.S., Holloway, H.C., & Hall, M. (2003). Terrorism with weapons of mass destruction: Chemical, biological, nuclear, radiological,and explosive agents. In R.J. Ursano and A.E. Norwood (Eds.), *Trauma and disaster: Responses and management* (pp. 125-154). Washington, DC: American Psychiatric Publishing.

U.S. Dept of Health and Human Services (2003). *Developing cultural competence in disaster mental health programs: Guiding principles and recommendations..* DHHS Pub #SMA3828. Rockville, MD: Center for Mental Health Services, SAMHSA.

U.S. Dept of Health and Human Services (2004). *Mental health response to mass violence and terrorism.* DHHS Pub #SAMA3959. Rockville, MD: Center for Mental Health Services, SAMHSA.

van der Hart, O., Brown, P., & van der Kolk, B. (1989). Pierre Janet's treatment of posttraumatic stress. *Journal of Traumatic Stress, 2,*379-396.

van der Veer, R., van Ijzendoorn, M. & Valsiner, J. (Eds.; 1994). Reconstructing the mind. *Replicability in research on human development.* Norwood, NJ: Ablex.

van Emmerick, A., Kamphuis, J., Hulsbosch, A., & Emmelkamp, P. (2002). Single session debriefing after psychological trauma: A meta-analysis. *Lancet,* 360, 766-771.

Verhoff, J., Kulka, R.A., & Couvan, E. (1981). *Mental health in America: Patterns of health seeking from 1957-1976.* New York: Basic Books.

Watson, P. Shalev, A. (2005). Assessment and treatment of adult acute responses to traumatic stress following mass traumatic events. *CNS Spectrum*, 123-131.

Watts, J. (1999). Tokyo terrorist attacks: Effects still felt 4 years on. *Lancet, 353*, 552-569.

Weaver, A.J. (1995). Has there been a failure to prepare and support parish-based clergy in their role as frontline community mental health workers? A review. *Journal of Pastoral Care. 49*, 129-49

Wee, D.F., Mills, D.M. & Koelher, G. (1999). The effects of Critical Incident Stress Debriefing on emergency medical services personnel following the Los Angeles civil disturbance. *International Journal of Emergency Mental Health, 1*, 33-38.

Weisaeth, L. (1989). A study of behavioral responses to an industrial disaster. *Acta Psychiatrica Scandinavica, Supp. 355, 80*, 13-24.

Wessely, S. & Deahl, M. (2003). In debate: Psychological debriefing is a waste of time. *British Journal of Psychiatry, 183*, 12-14.

Wessely, S., Rose, S., & Bisson, J. (1998). A systematic review of brief psychological interventions (debriefing) for the treatment of immediate trauma related symptoms and the prevention of post traumatic stress disorder (Cochrane Review). *Cochrane Library*, Issue 3, Oxford, UK: Update Software.

Western Management Consultants. (1996). *The Medical Services Branch CISM evaluation report*. Vancouver, BC: Author.

Wollman, D. (1993). Critical Incident Stress Debriefing and crisis groups: A review of literature. *Group, 17*, 70-83.

World Health Organization (2003). *Mental health in emergencies*. Geneva: Author.

Yalom, I. (1970). *Theory and practice of Group psychotherapy*. NY: Basic books.

INDEX